**ENVIRONMENTAL REMEDIAT
REGULATIONS AND SAFETY**

ECOSYSTEM RESTORATION

SELECTED PROGRAMS AND FEDERAL ACTIVITIES

Environmental Remediation Technologies, Regulations and Safety

ENVIRONMENTAL REMEDIATION TECHNOLOGIES,
REGULATIONS AND SAFETY

ECOSYSTEM RESTORATION

SELECTED PROGRAMS
AND FEDERAL ACTIVITIES

SIMON ACHESON
EDITOR

New York

For permission to use material from this book please contact us:
Telephone 631-231-7269; Fax 631-231-8175
Web Site: http://www.novapublishers.com

NOTICE TO THE READER

The Publisher has taken reasonable care in the preparation of this book, but makes no expressed or implied warranty of any kind and assumes no responsibility for any errors or omissions. No liability is assumed for incidental or consequential damages in connection with or arising out of information contained in this book. The Publisher shall not be liable for any special, consequential, or exemplary damages resulting, in whole or in part, from the readers' use of, or reliance upon, this material. Any parts of this book based on government reports are so indicated and copyright is claimed for those parts to the extent applicable to compilations of such works.

Independent verification should be sought for any data, advice or recommendations contained in this book. In addition, no responsibility is assumed by the publisher for any injury and/or damage to persons or property arising from any methods, products, instructions, ideas or otherwise contained in this publication.

This publication is designed to provide accurate and authoritative information with regard to the subject matter covered herein. It is sold with the clear understanding that the Publisher is not engaged in rendering legal or any other professional services. If legal or any other expert assistance is required, the services of a competent person should be sought. FROM A DECLARATION OF PARTICIPANTS JOINTLY ADOPTED BY A COMMITTEE OF THE AMERICAN BAR ASSOCIATION AND A COMMITTEE OF PUBLISHERS.

Additional color graphics may be available in the e-book version of this book.

Library of Congress Cataloging-in-Publication Data

ISBN: 978-1-63117-540-4

Published by Nova Science Publishers, Inc. † New York

CONTENTS

PREFACE

Lake Tahoe lies in the center of the Basin, and receives flows of melting water from snow caps of the surrounding mountain peaks. The Tahoe Basin contains wetlands, swamps, deep-water habitats, aspen stands, conifer forests, and meadows which harbor over 1,300 species of plants and animals. Environmental problems in the Tahoe Basin have led to federal, state, local, and private investments in ecosystem restoration. This book elaborates on the management and restoration activities in the Lake Tahoe Basin. It also discusses restoration of several other ecosystems that include the Salton Sea in California, the Great Lakes, and the Everglades in Florida.

Chapter 1 – The Lake Tahoe Basin (Basin) straddles the California-Nevada border and includes Lake Tahoe. The Basin is regarded for its beauty, wildlife diversity, clear waters, and recreation. Logging and mining stimulated development in the Basin beginning in the 1850s. Development, especially urban development, has affected the Basin's ecosystem, leading to a decline in the water quality of Lake Tahoe, tree mortality, heightened wildfire risk, and population declines in fish and wildlife species. Restoration of the Tahoe Basin began in 1969 under the Bi-State Compact between California and Nevada. The Compact authorized the creation of the Tahoe Regional Planning Agency (TRPA). TRPA oversees restoration efforts in the Tahoe Basin and monitors environmental progress, among other things. TRPA also created the Regional Plan, which is a framework for restoration. The Plan has specific goals for restoration, and focuses on improving water quality, decreasing the number of invasive species, maintaining populations and habitats of sensitive and listed species, and reducing wildfire risk in the surrounding forests. The implementation and funding of the Plan is done by state, federal, local, and private stakeholders. The federal government is involved in the restoration of the Basin due to its land holdings and funding for restoration. Federal agencies coordinate their efforts with other stakeholders through the Lake Tahoe Federal Interagency Partnership. In total, various entities have contributed over $1.7 billion to fund 600 projects since 1997. This includes approximately $554.5 million in federal funds. An additional $2.5 billion has been requested from stakeholders to fund an additional 700 projects from 2008 to 2018. The federal government has been asked to contribute $645 million of this newly planned spending. Currently, federal support for restoration projects has been authorized under the Lake Tahoe Restoration Act of 2000 (P.L. 106-506) and the Southern Nevada Public Lands Management Act (SNPLMA; P.L. 105-263). Views on the progress of restoration in the Basin have been mixed. Some local groups question whether funds have been efficiently spent, whereas others contend that progress has been significant in restoring the Basin ecosystem. These might change due to a recent update of the Regional Plan. This update appears to support sustainable development in the Basin, which has caused some environmental groups to question whether progress in restoring the Basin might be stalled. Others, however, contend that sustainable development and economic well-being of the region is necessary for ecosystem restoration in the long term. Another restoration issue is funding. Mandatory federal funding provided under SNPLMA is exhausted, causing some to question whether federal funding will remain at consistent levels or decline. The 113th Congress is attempting to address some of these issues in proposed legislation. S. 1451 would reauthorize $415 million for restoration for 10 fiscal years from the year enacted; promote federal support for scientific work in the Basin, including studies on the effects of climate change on the ecosystem; and authorize a program to address aquatic invasive species. Congress might also conduct oversight to understand the progress of restoration and provide input on current controversies concerning the balance between development and the environment in the Basin.

Chapter 2 – The Salton Sea is located in southern California and is considered the largest inland water body in the state. The Salton Basin, where the Salton Sea is located, has supported many lakes and water bodies throughout its geological history. The Salton Sea was created when a canal gate broke in 1905 allowing fresh Colorado River water into the Basin. The Salton Sea is now sustained by agricultural runoff from farmlands in the Imperial and Coachella valleys. It provides permanent and temporary habitat for many species of plants and animals, including several endangered species. It also serves as an important recreational area for the region. The Salton Sea has been altered by increasing salinity and decreasing size caused by steadily decreasing water flows into the Sea. High salinity levels and shrinking area have been linked to habitat changes and stressed populations of plants and animals, economic losses in the region, and impaired air quality. Efforts to restore the Salton Sea ecosystem have been discussed and initiated through state and federal actions. Several studies by state and federal agencies have provided baseline data about the Sea, and some restoration plans have been proposed. The State of California, the Salton Sea Authority, and the federal government through the Bureau of Reclamation have devised plans for restoring the Sea. However, none of these plans are being fully implemented. Federal authorities that address restoration of the Salton Sea are generally based on creating and evaluating proposals for restoration, rather than implementing restoration activities in a comprehensive manner similar to other initiatives in the Everglades and Great Lakes. California is pursuing restoration options, but funding for implementing them is lacking. Whether or not to restore the Salton Sea remains controversial. Proponents of restoration contend that the Salton Sea ecosystem is valuable from an ecological standpoint because it is one of the few remaining large-scale wetland habitats in California for migratory birds and fish. Further, some argue that keeping the Salton Sea intact will stimulate economic development, recreation, and tourism in the region. They note that losing the Sea could cause economic and environmental decline, and could lead to air quality problems from exposed seabeds. Others contend that the Sea should not be restored. They argue that the Salton Sea is naturally declining, as it has throughout its geological history. Further, they note that countering this process will be costly and ultimately not worth the expense. They state that limited restoration funds should be used to restore other natural wetlands in California, such as the Sacramento-San Joaquin Bay Delta. The decline of the Salton Sea ecosystem is accelerating due to water transfers from agricultural lands to municipal water districts in San Diego under the terms of the Quantification Settlement Agreement, an agreement on how to share California's apportionment of Colorado River water. The water transfers have resulted in less water flowing into the Salton Sea and accelerated increases in salinity and shoreline recession. According to some scientists, salinity levels may reach lethal levels for most fish and wildlife as soon as 2018. These predictions, along with the steadily declining ecosystem might provoke Congress to consider a larger role in restoration for the federal government. Congress may decide to address restoration by increasing the federal role in restoration efforts. This could be done by funding existing federal authorities that address, or could address, restoring the ecosystem; authorizing federal participation and appropriations for implementing existing restoration plans; or authorizing a new comprehensive plan to be created that might involve participation from federal and non-federal stakeholders, similar to other restoration initiatives around the country. Congress might also decide not to address restoration of the Salton Sea ecosystem, or simply maintain the status quo of federal participation.

Chapter 3 – The Great Lakes ecosystem is recognized by many as an international natural resource that has been altered by human activities and climate variability. These alterations have led to degraded water quality, diminished habitat, lower native fish and wildlife populations, and an altered ecosystem. In response, the federal governments of the United States and Canada and the state and provincial governments in the Great Lakes basin are implementing several restoration activities. These activities range from mitigating the harmful effects of toxic substances in lake waters to restoring fish habitat. Most laws and efforts in the past addressed specific issues in the Great Lakes; a few addressed issues at the ecosystem level. This caused the Government Accountability Office and others to express the need for initiating and implementing a comprehensive approach for restoring the Great Lakes ecosystem. In 2010, the Great Lakes Restoration Initiative (GLRI) was proposed and implemented by the Obama Administration. The aim of GLRI is to restore the Great Lakes ecosystem under one initiative. Specifically, the GLRI is to restore and maintain the chemical, physical and biological integrity of the Great Lakes Basin Ecosystem by directing activities to address five focus areas: (1) toxic substances and Areas of Concern (these are areas in the Great Lakes that are environmentally degraded); (2) invasive species; (3) nearshore health and nonpoint source pollution; (4) habitat and wildlife protection and restoration; and (5) accountability, monitoring, evaluation, communication, and partnerships. The Environmental Protection Agency (EPA) is the lead federal agency for implementing and administering GLRI. The EPA has received authority to distribute appropriated funds to several federal agencies, which then undertake restoration activities and projects. The EPA also administers grant programs to fund nonfederal projects and activities related to restoration. An interagency Great Lakes Task Force oversees the implementation of GLRI and created a strategy to guide restoration. The strategy (referred to as the Action Plan) provides a framework for restoring the Great Lakes ecosystem under GLRI from 2010 through 2014. For each focus area under the GLRI, the Action Plan provides a problem statement, a set of goals, interim objectives, progress measures, final targets, and principal activities for restoring the ecosystem. Restoration activities are being done under existing federal authorities. The GLRI has received approximately $1.37 billion in appropriated funds since FY2010. The scope and scale of this restoration initiative have led some to question its direction and duration. The GLRI does not specify what a restored ecosystem might look like, nor does it estimate how long restoration activities will need to be conducted, and how much restoration might cost. Some other questions surrounding this initiative include how the GLRI is governed and how federal and state restoration efforts are coordinated. Furthermore, GLRI remains an administrative initiative; there is no law that specifically authorizes GLRI, though Congress has appropriated funds to implement the program. Congress might consider these questions in oversight hearings or in legislation during the 113th Congress. Companion bills have been introduced in the 113th Congress to address GLRI. S. 1232 and H.R. 2773 would establish an administrative and management structure for restoration activities in the Great Lakes, authorize GLRI and appropriations for its implementation, specify the scope and function of GLRI, and authorize the coordinating role of the Great Lakes Interagency Task Force.

Chapter 4 – The Everglades is a unique network of subtropical wetlands in South Florida that is approximately half of its historical size, due in part to degradation from federal water projects. In 2000, Congress authorized a 30-year plan, termed the Comprehensive Everglades Restoration Plan (CERP), for the restoration of the Everglades ecosystem in southern Florida. When originally authorized, it was estimated that CERP would cost a total of $8.2 billion and take approximately 30 years to complete. More recent estimates indicate that the plan would take approximately 50 years to implement, and would cost $13.5 billion. Under CERP, the federal government (through the U.S. Army Corps of Engineers and the Department of the Interior) is required to fund half of the costs for restoration, with an array of state, tribal, and local agencies paying the other half. In addition to activities under CERP, a number of other federal and state efforts that pre-date CERP (known collectively as "non-CERP," or "Foundation" activities) also contribute to Everglades restoration. While non-CERP efforts are technically not included in CERP, the two sets of activities are widely viewed as complementary. Since passage of CERP in 2000, the federal investment in the Everglades has increased. As of the end of FY2012, the federal government had provided about $1 billion in funding for CERP, with the state providing matching funds for CERP projects, as well as advanced funding for land acquisition and construction for expected future CERP projects. Federal funding for non-CERP activities (most of which pre-date CERP) has also continued over this time period. These efforts are estimated to total more than $3 billion as of 2012. While estimates of nonfederal (i.e., state) funding contributions to CERP and related restoration efforts vary widely depending on what methodology and assumptions are used, most agree that to date, the state of Florida has spent significantly more on Everglades restoration than has the federal government. Progress has been made on a number of Everglades restoration projects, although overall progress to date has fallen short of initial goals. As of 2013, the majority of the land necessary for restoration projects under CERP had been acquired, and significant progress has been made on non-CERP activities (including improved water deliveries to Everglades National Park). Construction has also been initiated on four CERP projects, and studies have been completed or are underway for a number of other CERP projects. Despite this progress, some projects have seen setbacks in the form of schedule delays and cost escalations. Additionally, new or revised authorizations will be required for many projects to go forward. These impediments may have the effect of further delaying restoration efforts. Reductions to state funding and the status of potential new CERP project authorizations under in the proposed Water Resources Development Act (S. 601) have increased attention to the congressional role in facilitating Everglades restoration during the 113th Congress. Debate and resolution of these issues has implications, both for ecosystem restoration in the Everglades and for large-scale restoration initiatives elsewhere. This report provides information on federal funding for Everglades restoration. It also provides a brief overview of some of the accomplishments and potential challenges for Everglades restoration.

In: Ecosystem Restoration
Editor: Simon Acheson

ISBN: 978-1-63117-540-4
© 2014 Nova Science Publishers, Inc.

Chapter 1

OVERVIEW OF MANAGEMENT AND RESTORATION ACTIVITIES IN THE LAKE TAHOE BASIN[*]

*Pervaze A. Sheikh, Charles V. Stern
and Amanda Marie Levin*

SUMMARY

The Lake Tahoe Basin (Basin) straddles the California-Nevada border and includes Lake Tahoe. The Basin is regarded for its beauty, wildlife diversity, clear waters, and recreation. Logging and mining stimulated development in the Basin beginning in the 1850s. Development, especially urban development, has affected the Basin's ecosystem, leading to a decline in the water quality of Lake Tahoe, tree mortality, heightened wildfire risk, and population declines in fish and wildlife species.

Restoration of the Tahoe Basin began in 1969 under the Bi-State Compact between California and Nevada. The Compact authorized the creation of the Tahoe Regional Planning Agency (TRPA). TRPA oversees restoration efforts in the Tahoe Basin and monitors environmental progress, among other things. TRPA also created the Regional Plan, which is a framework for restoration. The Plan has specific goals for restoration, and focuses on improving water

---

[*] This is an edited, reformatted and augmented version of a Congressional Research Service publication, CRS Report for Congress R43224, dated September 13, 2013.

quality, decreasing the number of invasive species, maintaining populations and habitats of sensitive and listed species, and reducing wildfire risk in the surrounding forests. The implementation and funding of the Plan is done by state, federal, local, and private stakeholders.

The federal government is involved in the restoration of the Basin due to its land holdings and funding for restoration. Federal agencies coordinate their efforts with other stakeholders through the Lake Tahoe Federal Interagency Partnership. In total, various entities have contributed over $1.7 billion to fund 600 projects since 1997. This includes approximately $554.5 million in federal funds. An additional $2.5 billion has been requested from stakeholders to fund an additional 700 projects from 2008 to 2018. The federal government has been asked to contribute $645 million of this newly planned spending. Currently, federal support for restoration projects has been authorized under the Lake Tahoe Restoration Act of 2000 (P.L. 106-506) and the Southern Nevada Public Lands Management Act (SNPLMA; P.L. 105-263).

Views on the progress of restoration in the Basin have been mixed. Some local groups question whether funds have been efficiently spent, whereas others contend that progress has been significant in restoring the Basin ecosystem. These might change due to a recent update of the Regional Plan. This update appears to support sustainable development in the Basin, which has caused some environmental groups to question whether progress in restoring the Basin might be stalled. Others, however, contend that sustainable development and economic well-being of the region is necessary for ecosystem restoration in the long term. Another restoration issue is funding. Mandatory federal funding provided under SNPLMA is exhausted, causing some to question whether federal funding will remain at consistent levels or decline.

The 113th Congress is attempting to address some of these issues in proposed legislation. S. 1451 would reauthorize $415 million for restoration for 10 fiscal years from the year enacted; promote federal support for scientific work in the Basin, including studies on the effects of climate change on the ecosystem; and authorize a program to address aquatic invasive species. Congress might also conduct oversight to understand the progress of restoration and provide input on current controversies concerning the balance between development and the environment in the Basin.

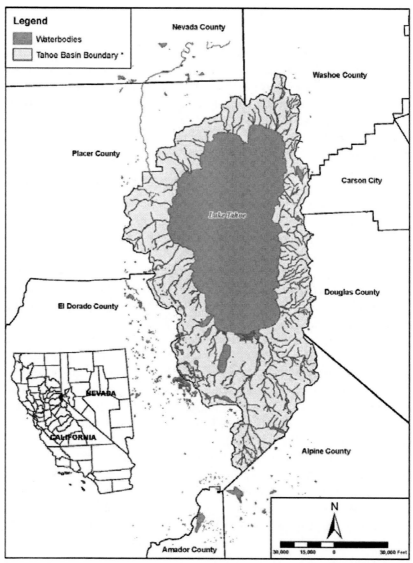

Source: U.S. Army Corps of Engineers. 2009. Lake Tahoe Region Aquatic Invasive
Species Management Plan, California-Nevada.

Figure 1. Lake Tahoe Map.

INTRODUCTION

The Lake Tahoe Basin (Tahoe Basin) extends across California and Nevada, bordered by the Sierra Nevada Mountains on the west and the Carson Range on the east (see **Figure 1**). Lake Tahoe lies in the center of the Basin, and receives flows of melting water from snow caps of the surrounding mountain peaks. The Tahoe Basin contains wetlands, swamps, deep-water habitats, aspen stands, conifer forests, and meadows which harbor over 1,300 species of plants and animals.[1] Tahoe Basin's natural environment contributes to the development of the area's $5 billion economy.[2] Part of this contribution is through recreation: over 3 million people visit Tahoe annually to ski, hike, bike, fish, and gamble, among other things. Development in the Tahoe Basin has affected its ecosystem. In the late 1800s, over 60% of the Basin forests were clear-cut.[3] Continued logging and clear-cutting have led to forest stands that are highly susceptible to drought, disease, insects, and fire.[4] In addition, water clarity in Lake Tahoe has declined by more than a third since 1967 due primarily to agricultural and urban run-off.[5] Lake Tahoe is also increasingly threatened by aquatic invasive species (AIS), which outcompete many of the native species in the lake.

Environmental problems in the Tahoe Basin have led to federal, state, local, and private investments in ecosystem restoration. The federal and state governments began to acquire land in the Tahoe Basin in 1969 to protect, maintain, and restore the ecology of the area. Public acquisition and protection of land in the Tahoe Basin continues today. As of 2011, approximately 87% of the Tahoe Basin is publicly owned. The largest shareholder is the U.S. Department of Agriculture (USDA), which owns 78% (154,000 acres and 508 miles of roads).[6] U.S. Forest Service (USFS), as part of USDA, maintains forests, roads, and trails on their federal lands in the Tahoe Basin. In addition to land acquisition, resources have also been dedicated for restoration efforts. Nearly 414 restoration projects have been completed in the Tahoe Basin and another 194 are ongoing since 1997. As of FY2013, total funding for restoration was $1.69 billion, of which $554.5 million was from the federal government.[7]

There have been multiple federal programs to improve the environmental and economic health in the Tahoe Basin. The Lake Tahoe Restoration Act of 2000 (LTRA) states that there is a federal responsibility to restore environmental health to the Basin. In addition, under Executive Order 13057 (*Federal Actions in the Lake Tahoe Region*), the U.S. Environmental Protection Agency (EPA), Department of Defense (DOD), Department of

Transportation (DOT), Department of Interior (DOI), and USDA are directed to help states preserve and maintain the environmental and economic viability of the area through funding, leadership, stewardship, and collaboration.[8] Congress has played a role in providing funding for federal collaboration in the Basin in the past. In 2000, Congress passed the Lake Tahoe Restoration Act (TRPA) (P.L. 106-506), which authorized $300 million for restoration in Lake Tahoe for 10 years. These funds were appropriated in 2003 as part of a series of amendments to the Southern Nevada Public Lands Management Act (SNPLMA) (P.L. 105-263).[9] Other restoration funding has been provided through agency base appropriations.

BACKGROUND ON LAKE TAHOE BASIN

The Tahoe Basin covers 505 square miles, or 323,200 acres, across the California-Nevada border. Around three-fourths of the Tahoe Basin is in California and one-fourth is in Nevada.[10] The Tahoe Basin is best known for the clear, blue waters of Lake Tahoe. Lake Tahoe is one of the oldest and purest lakes in the world. It is also the second-deepest lake in the country.[11] Lake Tahoe is designated an Outstanding National Resource Water (ONRW) by the Environmental Protection Agency (EPA).[12] This title is reserved for waters with exceptional recreational or ecological significance. All waters designated as an ONRW receive special protection against degradation under both state water quality standards and the Clean Water Act (CWA).[13] Lake Tahoe covers 191 square miles of the Basin and holds around 39 trillion gallons of fresh water. Around 212 billion gallons of fresh water enter the lake each year from its 63 tributaries (65%) and direct precipitation (35%).[14] Water exits either through evaporation or through the Truckee River, the only tributary flowing out of the lake. The flow of water from the lake into this river is regulated by the Lake Tahoe Dam.[15]

The Tahoe Basin is made up of several ecological habitats, including wetlands, meadows, aspen stands, conifer forests, deciduous riparian lands, shrub land, swamps, deep-water aquatic habitat, marshes, and fens (peat-forming wetlands).[16] The Tahoe Basin also serves as a stop along the Pacific Flyway, which many endangered waterfowl use during migration. An estimated 55 animal species and 43 plants and fungi are state (species of special interest or sensitive species) or federally listed (endangered or threatened).[17] Multiple protected areas and management plans have been implemented around the Tahoe Basin to address federally listed species.[18]

Environmental Concerns in Tahoe Basin

There are four primary environmental concerns in the Tahoe Basin: water pollution, drought, invasive species, and land use. These issues are interconnected and, in some cases, influence one another. This section provides brief background and discusses these environmental concerns.

Water Pollution in Lake Tahoe

Background

Lake Tahoe is classified as an ultra-oligotrophic lake, which is characterized by very low levels of nutrients, specifically phosphorous and nitrogen.[19] Ultra-oligotrophic lakes have low algal production, which often results in clear water with high levels of oxygen and water quality suitable for drinking.[20] The high levels of oxygen in ultra-oligotrophic lakes can support many fish species and create a complex underwater ecosystem. While Lake Tahoe still meets the criteria of ultra-oligotrophic, there are concerns about the future trophic status due to water pollution and runoff.[21]

Over time, ultra-oligotrophic lakes are generally expected to become less oligotrophic. Eutrophication (resulting from excessive amounts of nutrients) is a slow, natural part of lake aging that occurs from natural buildup of dead and decaying organisms.[22] However, eutrophication in Lake Tahoe has been accelerated, in part, by human activities, such as urban run-off, fertilizer use, car exhaust, and introduced species.[23] Eutrophication leads to increased algal productivity and loss of water quality, which can lead to fish kills and odor issues.[24]

Concerns

Lake Tahoe is considered an impaired water body under CWA due to marked decline in the quality and clarity of the water. The water quality of Lake Tahoe has been declining since the 1960s. Water clarity is used as a proxy of the Lake's water quality.[25] Lake Tahoe has lost around 33% of its clarity since 1968 due to fine particles, phosphorous, and nitrogen entering the water.

As shown in **Figure 2**, the clarity was measured to be 102 ft in 1968; by 2011, the clarity had decreased to 68.9 ft, increasing to 75.3 ft in 2012.[26] Fine particles and phosphorous enter the lake mainly through run-off from urban and non-urban watersheds; nitrogen enters the lake mainly thorough atmospheric deposition.[27]

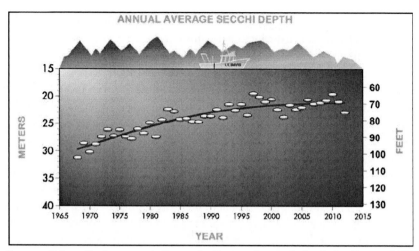

Source: Tahoe Environmental Research Center, State of the Lake Report 2013,
        Published August 2013.

Figure 2. Clarity Levels Since 1968.

The designation of Lake Tahoe as an impaired water body requires that a
Total Maximum Daily Load (TMDL) be established as part of a management
plan to bring Lake Tahoe back into compliance with CWA.[28] The final TMDL
for Lake Tahoe was approved by the EPA in 2011. The TMDL addresses three
main water pollutants: fine particles, nitrogen, and phosphorus.[29] Fine particles
in the lake are the main contributor to clarity decline, with 72% of all particles
coming from urban runoff.[30] The compliance standard for the lake is set at
measured clarity of 97.4 ft.[31] This standard has never been reached since the
adoption of the TMDL, and the EPA estimates that it will take 65 years after
implementation of TMDLs to reach compliance.[32]

Wildfires

Background
The forests in the Tahoe Basin were originally sparse, pine-dominated
areas.[33] However, many of the pine stands were clear-cut at the end of the 19th
century to provide timber for nearby mining towns. Due to these past logging
activities, the forests are now considered overly dense and fir dominated.[34] The
current nutrient and moisture levels in the soil can only support one healthy
tree for every three trees that now grow.[35] This high density contributes to tree

disease, insect infestation, and tree mortality. In addition, fir trees are not well-suited for drought. It is estimated that a third of the forest in the Tahoe Basin has been killed from insects or drought.[36] The number of dead trees, altered composition of the forest, and density of trees contribute to portions of the Tahoe Basin being considered extreme or very high wildfire hazard areas.[37] Regional drought conditions also contribute to increased wildfire risk in the Tahoe Basin.

Concerns

The current fuel load (or availability of combustible organic material) in Tahoe Basin forests has created concern among land managers that any forest fire could be devastating to both the environment and surrounding communities. While fire and regeneration are part of the normal ecosystem cycle for many forests, some estimate that fires under current conditions could have severe negative economic effects as well as environmental effects. For example, the last fire in the Tahoe Basin cost $11.3 million to control, and resulted in over $141 million in damages and over $1 billion in lost economic revenue.[38] In addition, the ash from wildfires and runoff from burnt lands can have negative impacts on the water quality of the lake, and can destroy critical habitat for endangered and native species.[39]

Invasive Species

Background

There are at least 20 established non-native species in the Tahoe Basin. While there are terrestrial invasive species, such as cheatgrass and other weeds, a majority of concerns focus on aquatic invasive species (AIS). Current documented AIS in the lake include the Asian clam, the zebra mussel, Eurasian watermilfoil, curlyleaf pondweed, the largemouth bass, and the bluegill.[40] These aquatic weeds, clams, snails, and warm-water fish have been both purposefully and accidently introduced into Lake Tahoe. These AIS have contributed to large shifts in the ecology of the lake. Historically, there was only one native predatory fish in Lake Tahoe, the Lahontan cutthroat trout (*Oncorhynchus clarkiihenshawi*).[41] However, this native trout is no longer found in the lake due to AIS and has been replaced by non-native mackinaw and other lake trout. Similar declines and losses of native minnows and crustaceans have been recorded, and some have attributed their decline to AIS.[42]

Concerns

AIS lead to water quality degradation; loss of native species and habitat; destruction of water conveyance systems; and economic losses.[43] Once established, invasive species can have significant economic and environmental costs. The economic impact of new AIS introductions or expansions of current AIS in Lake Tahoe is estimated to have a present value of $417.5 million over a 50-year period.[44] In addition, the Asian Clam (*Corbicula fluminea*) is replacing native pea clams and now comprises almost half of the sediment-dwelling organisms in some areas.[45] Asian clam beds are breeding grounds for the green alga Zygnema, which increase the phosphorous levels in the lakes, contributing to water quality decline.[46] According to the National Invasive Species Council, the most cost-effective way to fight invasive species is through preventing them from entering the ecosystem.[47] This philosophy is being applied to temper the concern that Quagga mussels may be introduced from Lake Mead and established in Lake Tahoe. Prevention has become a large focus for many agencies in the Tahoe region after the invasive Quagga Mussel was found in neighboring Lake Mead in 2007.[48] Since 2008, the Tahoe Regional Planning Agency, in conjunction with the U.S. Fish and Wildlife Service, has been requiring inspections and decontamination of all boats entering Lake Tahoe as a preventative measure. If Quagga mussels enter Lake Tahoe, they could alter the food web, promote the growth of algae, clog water intake pipes, and affect boats. In addition, efforts to eliminate the mussels from the lake would likely involve the use of rubber mats and other technology, which would be expensive and could lead to residual harm of the lake's ecosystem.

Land Use

Background

There was substantial development in the Tahoe Basin as a result of the 1960 Winter Olympics in Squaw Valley, especially during the 1970s. Development occurred throughout the Tahoe Basin and often occurred on sensitive lands, such as wetlands or riparian areas. From 1981 until 1987, sequential long-term moratoriums were placed on development due to degradation of the lake, which had been associated with increased urban development. The final moratorium was lifted with the passage of the Regional Plan for restoration in 1987.

The Plan included a strict new approval process and oversight of new development in the area (see section below on "The Regional Plan" for more details). Development that occurred before the passage of the 1987 Regional Plan is termed legacy construction.

Concerns

Many of the water quality, air quality, and habitat degradation issues facing the Tahoe Basin are amplified by legacy construction. Due to restrictions on redevelopment and renovation after 1987, a large portion of the development in the Tahoe Basin is aging and located in environmentally sensitive areas. These older buildings often do not have best management practices (BMPs) installed for controlling runoff, which can lead to increased urban runoff and watershed deterioration. The Tahoe Regional Planning Agency estimates that 90% of existing homes and businesses in the Tahoe Basin were built without considerations for environmental design.[49] In addition, the reliance of automobiles and road development due to land use patterns also may contribute to urban runoff, watershed deterioration, and air quality issues, according to some.[50]

RESTORATION OF LAKE TAHOE

The restoration of Lake Tahoe is a complex issue due to the large number of stakeholder groups involved. There are 50 federal, state, local, and private groups that are involved in current restoration plans and projects (see **Figure 3**). Restoration in the Tahoe Basin is overseen by a regional entity, the Tahoe Regional Planning Agency (TRPA), and guided by a comprehensive plan termed the Regional Plan.

The Regional Plan includes nine environmental thresholds; each threshold has multiple specific, quantitative, outcome-based goals that the Tahoe Basin must attain to meet the threshold. To help meet these thresholds, TRPA, in conjunction with the federal government, created the Environmental Improvement Program (EIP).

The EIP is a capital improvement program and is updated every 10 years to reflect new environmental issues or concerns in the Tahoe Basin. Within the EIP, there is a list of approved projects to be funded and implemented by state, local, private, and federal partners over a five-year horizon. This five-year list serves as one of the primary guiding documents for federal restoration efforts and collaboration in the Basin.

Federal agencies involved in restoration efforts in the Tahoe Basin include DOI (Bureau of Reclamation), DOT (Federal Highway Administration and

Federal Transit Authority), USDA (USFS and Natural Resources Conservation Service), DOD (Army Corps of Engineers), and the EPA. Each state has one agency that leads collaboration efforts with federal and regional entities. California state efforts are led by the California Tahoe Conservancy (CTC), housed in the California Natural Resources Agency. Nevada state efforts are led by the Nevada Division of State Lands, which is housed in the Nevada Department of Conservation and Natural Resources. Local stakeholders include local governments, environmental organizations, tribes, and private entities.[51]

In addition, state and federal entities, such as the University of California–Davis (through the Tahoe Environmental Research Center (TERC)), the University of Nevada–Reno, the U.S. Geological Survey (USGS), and the Desert Research Institute (DRI), monitor environmental indicators (e.g., air and water temperature, precipitation, snow melt, and clarity) and provide scientific information that aims to inform restoration and management actions and plans.

Compact and Tahoe Regional Planning Agency

In 1969, Congress ratified a Bi-State Compact between California and Nevada.[52] This Bi-State Compact of 1969 marked the beginning of the current collaborative restoration process in the Tahoe Basin. The main focus of this compact was to preserve and restore Lake Tahoe through public acquisition of lands.

Further, the Compact authorized the creation of the Tahoe Regional Planning Agency (TRPA). TRPA oversees restoration efforts in the Tahoe Basin and manages the implementation of the Regional Plan, as well as assesses overall environmental progress, among other things.

In December 1980, the 96th Congress amended the Bi-State Compact (P.L. 96-551) in response to worsening environmental conditions in the Tahoe Basin. The amended compact called for TRPA to develop environmental threshold carrying capacities (Thresholds), which set environmental goals and standards for the Tahoe Basin.[53] The Compact also required TRPA to develop a Regional Plan (Plan) to guide efforts to meet the Thresholds. The Plan was developed in 1987 based on nine environmental thresholds:[54]

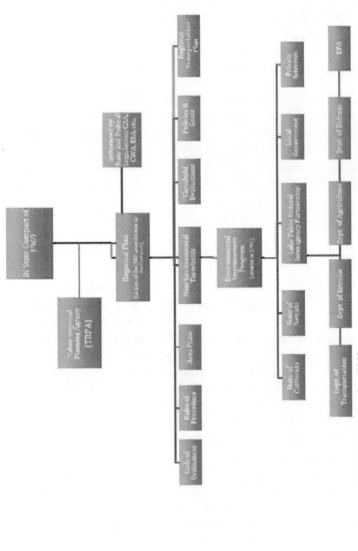

Source: Congressional Research Service, 2013.

Figure 3. Organizational Scheme of Lake Tahoe Restoration.

1. Water quality
   - Objectives include reducing fine sediment particles, phosphorous, and nitrogen levels (as set by the TMDL) to achieve annual average clarity of 97.4 feet or better; reducing and preventing the introduction of AIS.
2. Soil conservation
   - Objectives include restoring 25% of disturbed stream zones; reducing the total area of impervious surfaces (termed land coverage under the Plan).
3. Air quality
   - Objectives include achieving all air quality standards for CO, ozone, and particulates under the Clean Air Act; reducing traffic by 7% of the 1981 base levels; reducing vehicle miles traveled by 10% of the 1981 base year values.
4. Vegetation
   - Objectives include maintaining at least 4% meadow, wetland vegetation, and riparian vegetation in the Tahoe Basin; maintaining 15%-25% of the Yellow Pine Forest and Red Fir Forest; and maintaining a minimum number of population sites for some sensitive plant species.
5. Wildlife
   - Objectives include maintaining a minimum number of population sites for certain species and eliminating the degradation of significant wildlife habitat.
6. Fisheries
   - Objectives include maintaining 180 miles of pristine stream habitat; restoring 6,000 acres of lake habitat; and reintroducing Lahontan cutthroat trout.
7. Scenic resources
   - Objectives include maintaining or improving scenic travel route ratings, views of individual scenic resources, and quality of views from public recreation areas.
8. Recreation
   - Objectives include preserving high quality recreational experiences for the public.
9. Noise
   - Objectives include establishing maximum noise levels for aircraft, watercraft, motor vehicles, motorcycles, and other off-road vehicles.

TRPA is directed by a 15-member Governing Board composed of seven delegates from California, seven delegates from Nevada, and one non-voting Presidential Appointee.[55] Six of these members represent units of local government; the other eight voting members represent their respective states' interests. The Governing Board holds monthly meetings to approve projects, amend any part of the compact or Plan, and conduct other routine business.[56] In addition, the Governing Board receives technical and scientific assistance from the Advisory Planning Commission. This 21-member Commission is made up of local planners, members of the community, and subject experts.[57] In addition to its leadership role in restoration, TRPA also serves as the Tahoe Metropolitan Planning Organization (TMPO), which is tasked with establishing a safe, efficient, and integrated transportation system throughout the Basin.[58]

The Regional Plan

The main guiding document for restoration is the Regional Plan (Plan). The Plan is a regulatory framework that includes multiple policies and plans such as the Thresholds, the Goals and Policies created by TRPA to help achieve the Thresholds, the Code of Ordinances related to development in the Tahoe Basin, Rules of Procedure that govern the TRPA Board and staff, Area Plans for development and conservation, the Regional Transportation Plan, and the Threshold Evaluation Report.[59] The Environmental Improvement Program (EIP) is also part of the Plan, but serves as the implementation mechanism to achieve the environmental goals under each Threshold.

The Plan sets levels on potential new development to achieve the Thresholds. This allows, in part, TRPA to control and limit development in Lake Tahoe. Mechanisms for controlling development include a system of transferrable development rights, caps on land coverage and building height, and public ownership and acquisition programs.[60]

The Plan is updated periodically to reflect progress on achieving the Thresholds, new environmental concerns, any management plans required by federal laws such as the Clean Air Act (CAA) and CWA, and any federal, state, or local laws and regulations. Specifically, the Thresholds are evaluated every four years; the last evaluation was in 2011.[61] The evaluation serves as a monitoring program and is used to adapt and adjust restoration efforts in the Plan to better accomplish the Thresholds (see **Figure 4**). For example, Thresholds with the lowest levels of achievement may lead to prioritizing restoration projects to address those specific Threshold goals. In addition, Threshold goals, such as water quality, have been amended to reflect new legislation (i.e., TMDL requirements) and environmental concerns (i.e., AIS). The Plan was fully updated in December of 2012, and included amended versions of TRPA's "Goals and Policies" and "Code of Ordinances" following Governing Board approval (this is discussed in more detail under Future Restoration Efforts).

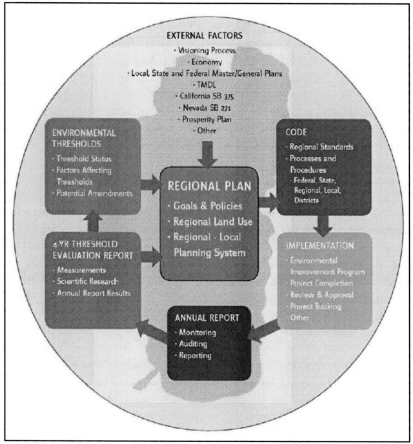

Source: Tahoe Regional Planning Agency. *Regional Plan Goals and Policies*. pp. 1-5.

Figure 4. Regional Plan Process Flow Chart.

Environmental Improvement Program

The Environmental Improvement Program (EIP) serves as the implementing mechanism for the Regional Plan. Through the EIP, TRPA and its partners identify, fund, and implement specific restoration projects in the Tahoe Basin. Within the EIP, TRPA develops and manages a separate list of capital projects, which are designed to achieve the environmental thresholds identified in the Plan. Further, this list is adaptively managed to allow for funding of new, unforeseen restoration projects that are necessary (e.g., environmental rehabilitation after the 2007 fire).[62] The projects on the list represent what TRPA believes can reasonably be funded and implemented over a five-year planning horizon. Thus, this capital project list is separately updated every five years.[63] The funding target, broader restoration goals, and focus areas of the EIP are only updated every 10 years by TRPA in response to the environmental and economic conditions of the Tahoe Basin. Since 1997, 414 projects have been completed and 194 projects are ongoing through the EIP.

The EIP was last updated in 2008, and identified over 700 new or ongoing projects that should receive funding and support through the EIP.[64] Planned EIP projects include efforts to improve water quality and watersheds, decrease automobile use, improve and increase habitat areas, and preserve species of interest. The updated EIP addresses new issues and focus areas through 2018, including water quality, habitat, and watershed improvements; fuel reduction and forest management; invasive species control; increased walkability and alternative transportation; and applied science, including climate change adaption and invasive species.[65] Nonfederal stakeholders contend that a portion of these focus areas may require federal participation.[66] Projects requiring federal collaboration may include efforts to treat an additional 68,000 acres of forest lands for fuel reduction; restore and recover the threatened Lahontan cutthroat trout to self- sustaining levels; retrofit 300 additional miles of roadways with water quality and watershed improvements; construct 43 miles of bike and pedestrian trails; rehabilitate and construct 40 recreational facilities; and improve stormwater management.[67]

Federal Involvement in the EIP

The five-year capital projects list currently includes 530 projects. Of these, more than half will receive federal funds or have a federal agency as an implementer.[68] Federal assistance with the EIP and its projects is mainly administered through the Lake Tahoe Federal Interagency Partnership (LTFIP). Agencies in the LTFIP are USDA, DOI, DOT, DOD, and EPA.

Created through Executive Order 13057 in 1997, LTFIP is directed to provide federal assistance and collaboration for EIP implementation. In addition, the executive order commits the federal government, through the participating federal departments and agencies, to help California and Nevada achieve the environmental standards for Lake Tahoe through collaboration and funding.[69] The agencies help with restoration of the Tahoe Basin through "stewardship, service, and science." The federal agencies have many roles in Lake Tahoe, including conducting research and studies, public outreach and education, regulation, funding, and implementing projects. These agencies mainly focus on watershed and habitat improvement, air quality and transportation, recreation and scenic improvements, and forest health.[70]

LTFIP is overseen by the regional administrators of the federal departments (known as the Tahoe Regional Executives).[71] However, most of the day-to-day activities involved in coordination and implementation are the responsibility of senior local agency officials for each federal agency.

Funding the EIP

Funding for the EIP comes from federal, state, local, and private groups. The original EIP (1997-2007) called for an initial investment of $908 million in capital projects and $58 million for research during its first 10 years. During this period it received $1.1 billion in funds from federal, state, local, and private stakeholders. The updated EIP has a funding target of an additional $2.45 billion to fund new programs between 2008 and 2018.[72] Of this, the federal government has been asked to provide $654 million.

In total, since the inception of the EIP (in 1997), the federal government has contributed $554.5 million to EIP restoration efforts. Total contributions from all EIP stakeholders (federal and nonfederal) are $1.69 billion as of July 2013 (see **Figure 5** for breakdown). For the second 10- year phase of the EIP (2008-2018), approximately $260 million has been committed by the federal government through agency appropriations and mandatory appropriations under the Southern Nevada Public Land Management Act (SNPLMA; P.L. 105-263). In total, approximately $600 million in funds have been committed by all parties for 2008-2018, as of July 2013.

Sources of federal funding for implementing the EIP come from discretionary and mandatory sources of funding. In 2001, Congress passed the Lake Tahoe Restoration Act of 2000 (LTRA; P.L. 106-506), authorizing $300 million in federal funds for the federal share of the EIP over the next 10 years.[73] These funds were appropriated under the 2003 amendments to SNPLMA, which provide no more than $300 million to the Secretary of the Interior to implement EIP projects. This is considered mandatory funding for restoration. SNPLMA receives funding from the selling of surplus federal public lands around Las Vegas.[74] In 2006, SNPLMA was amended to include a hazardous fuel reduction program, which would provide funding to agencies in the Tahoe Basin for hazardous fuels reduction activities.[75] In FY2012, SNPLMA completed its $300 million funding commitment to the EIP; no additional funding will be given to the EIP through SNPLMA as of FY2013 unless Congress authorizes new appropriations under LTRA. Reauthorization of appropriations under LTRA was proposed in the 113th Congress: S. 1451 (the Lake Tahoe Restoration Act of 2013) would authorize $415 million over 10 fiscal years after it was enacted.

(in $US millions)

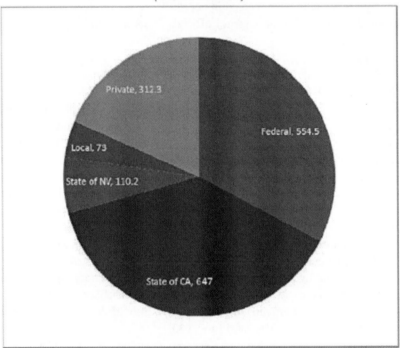

Source: TRPA, Lake Tahoe EIP Marks 15 years of Achievement. Press Release. August 16, 2013.

Figure 5. EIP Funding.

Table 1. Federal Funding of the Lake Tahoe Federal Partnership FY2002-2012
(In $millions, funds are for activities directly and indirectly related to restoration)

	FY 2002	FY 2003	FY 2004	FY 2005	FY 2006	FY 2007	FY 2008	FY 2009	FY 2010	FY 2011	FY 2012	Total Funding FY2002- FY2012
USFS	$16.9	$45.9	$29.9	$32.0	$47.3	$41.3	$41.5	$46.2	$33.5	$35.6	$28.7	$398.8
NRCS	0.5	0.8	0.9	1.2	1.6	1.8	2.0	0.1	0.4	0.9	0.2	$10.4
Corps	1.3	1.5	1.8	2.9	11.3	9.5	8.2	3.6	3.4	0.1	0.1	$43.7
USGS	1.9	1.9	1.6	2.0	1.2	0.8	1.0	0.7	0.7	0.8		$12.6
USDOT	23.3	0.4	9.0	24.9	5.6	5.9	19.2	40.9	29.0	21.5	10.3	$190.0
EPA	2.4	2.6	0.9	5.8	2.0	1.1	2.4	1.4	2.6	1.3	2.2	$24.7
FWS	0.2	0.2	0.2	0.4	0.3	0.3	0.7	0.8	2.3	3.9	3.5	$12.8
BOR	2.7	1.5	4.0	1.9	3.4	0.3	2.5	0.09	3.0	1.3	1.0	$21.7
[Total federal funding for EIP only]	[30.0]	[46.2]	[36.8]	[50.3]	[54.2]	[49.1]	[62.2]	[43.3]	[40.4]	[46.5]	[43.7]	[502.7]
Total	$49.1	$54.8	$48.3	$71.0	$72.7	$61.0	$77.4	$93.8	$75.0	$65.4	$45.0	$713.7

Source: Lake Tahoe Federal Interagency Partnership, Progress Report, Federal Actions at Lake Tahoe FY2006-2008, Lake Tahoe Federal Interagency Partnership, 2009, p. 28. Email from the Tahoe Regional Planning Authority, September 26, 2012 and August 23, 2013.

Notes: Abbreviations = U.S. Army Corps of Engineers (Corps), U.S. Bureau of Reclamation (BOR), U.S. Department of Transportation (USDOT), Environmental Protection Agency (EPA), U.S. Fish and Wildlife Service (FWS), U.S. Forest Service (USFS), U.S. Geological Survey (USGS), and Natural Resources Conservation Service (NRCS). EIP= Environmental Improvement Program.

Federal funding for restoration activities in Lake Tahoe also occurs outside of the EIP. The federal government has appropriated over $318 million for non-EIP federal agency actions in the Basin that are directly and indirectly related to restoration (see **Table 1** for last 10 years of federal funding).[76]

Other Federal Involvement

Complementary to the EIP, there are additional thresholds, goals, and related projects required by other federal legislation, such as the CWA Section 208 Water Management Plan and the Regional Transportation and Air Quality Management Plan (Mobility 2035), among others.

Lake Tahoe is subject to EPA oversight due to the lake's 303(d) designation and past carbon monoxide (CO) non-attainment. Impaired waters are placed on the 303(d) list and require the state and EPA to develop a TMDL and Water Management Plan. The Water Management Plan requires that basin-wide fine sediment particles, phosphorous, and nitrogen loads be reduced by 32%, 14%, and 4%, respectively, by 2028 and by 65%, 35%, and 10%, respectively to reach EPA's water quality standards by 2076.[77] To achieve this, the Water Quality Management Plan has identified the use of stream restoration projects as well as projects to reduce urban dust levels to lower urban runoff, along with requirements that all homes and businesses complete certified water quality Best Management Practices (BMPs) to control erosion and filter storm water.[78]

The Tahoe Basin also has developed a regional transportation and air quality management plan designed to maintain CAA standards.[79] The new Regional Transportation Plan, Mobility 2035, is required by state, regional, and federal laws, including California's SB375, the Bi-State Compact, and MAP-21.[80] Mobility 2035 provides funding for projects that encourage the development of walkable, mixed-use town centers, improved transit options, and reduced dependency on automobiles to meet water and air quality standards.[81] This will include work and improvements on federal roads, in part to meet both Bi-State compact thresholds and TMDL measures.[82]

The Fish and Wildlife Service (FWS) plays a role in the management and recovery of federally listed species in the basin, as well as the Aquatic Invasive Species (AIS) Program. FWS has implemented recovery plans for the Lahontan cutthroat trout under the Endangered Species Act (ESA) and monitors other federally listed species in the Tahoe Basin.[83] FWS is also involved in the monitoring and protection of nesting bald eagles and golden eagles as authorized by the Bald and Golden Eagle Protection Act (16 U.S.C §668). In addition, FWS has been appropriated $5 million since 2008 to implement an AIS program within the Tahoe Basin.[84] The AIS program inspects and, if necessary, decontaminates all boats entering the lake, in addition to funding pilot AIS eradication projects. FWS has developed an AIS Management Plan for the Lake and chairs the Lake Tahoe AIS Coordination Committee.

The U.S. Geological Survey (USGS) has created an Internet-based clearinghouse of scientific information on the Lake Tahoe Basin with Geographic Information System (GIS) capability.[85] USGS is involved in scientific research and monitoring activities in the Basin, partnering with federal and state agencies, as well as with research centers (e.g., TERC, University of Reno, DRI). USGS is part of the Tahoe Science Consortium, a collaboration between research organizations and federal agencies whose objective is to promote science and provide the best available scientific information to guide restoration and support adaptive management strategies within the Tahoe Basin.[86]

Measuring the Progress of Restoration

The progress of restoration in the Lake Tahoe Basin is measured through environmental quality indicators, such as water clarity, native fish populations, and number of bird nests. These indicators are extrapolated to measure the attainment of Threshold goals. Every four years, these data are combined and used to measure restoration progress and the attainment of each threshold. Findings are then published in the independently peer-reviewed Threshold Evaluation Report.[87]

The Threshold Evaluation was last completed in 2011; it found that a majority of the specific final goals established as indicators for the nine thresholds had been attained. However, only approximately two-thirds of all indicators could be quantifiably measured.[88] The status of the other one-third of the indicators is currently unknown. In addition, attainment for some indicators may not indicate actual environmental improvement. There are several types of indicators: numerical standards, management standards, and policy standards. Often management standards, while considered quantifiable, can only be evaluated based on whether a program has been implemented; attainment for these standards does not indicate that the program has led to actual achievement of a goal.

Some of the indicators with the highest levels of attainment were air quality, soil conservation and impervious cover, recreation facilities, and wildlife. In 2011, 361 days of the year were measured at highest air quality. The other four were measured at moderate air quality.[89] The threshold evaluation also found that all special interest species—both state and federally listed—had stable or improving populations. In particular, the projects for the Lahontan cutthroat trout, Tahoe yellow cress, and the golden eagle were recognized as successful. The winter water clarity of the Lake has improved the last few years, and modeling predicts that the winter clarity will continue to improve. The 2012 winter water clarity averaged at 88.7 ft, the best measurement since 1996. Annual water clarity averaged at 75.3 ft, the best in 10 years, marking the second consecutive year of improved annual clarity.[90]

Major accomplishments and projects completed in the Basin, as of 2013, include:[91]

- Fuels reduction treatment of over 54,248 acres of forests;
- Wildlife habitat improvements of 15,896 acres (including 1,509 acres in sensitive stream zones);
- 739 acres of wetlands restored;
- 3,103 acres of sensitive land acquired by public entities;
- Watershed improvements on 501 miles of roads;
- Renovation of 13,444 private homes to lower levels of urban runoff;
- 136 miles of new bike and pedestrian trails;
- Upgrades of 20 transit stations and increased transit ridership to 1.5 million people a year;
- Reintroduction and signs of recovery of the Tahoe yellow cress and Lahontan cutthroat trout;
- 29,000 watercraft inspections and over 10,000 watercraft decontaminations; and
- Treatment of 24 acres of weeds and Asian clam infestations in Lake Tahoe.

While some point to these accomplishments as signs of success, others contend that much more needs to be done. TRPA cites increasing algal productivity, declining summer clarity, increasing wildfire threat, and the increasing presence of invasive species as areas of concern.[92] The reasons for and the solutions to these continued issues with summer and nearshore lake clarity, phytoplankton and algal productivity, swamp habitats, and invasive species are still contested. Some local environmental groups argue that current restoration doesn't do enough to address the causes of environmental degradation; others assert that the issues persist due to warming patterns in the region which cannot be resolved exclusively through restoration.[93] Notably, while there have been improvements in annual lake clarity, clarity still needs to improve by more than another 20 feet to reach the clarity standard set by the EPA under the TMDL.

Future Restoration Efforts

After more than seven years of preparation, discussion, and development with stakeholders, the Regional Plan was updated in December 2012 for the first time since its passage in 1987.[94] The updated Regional Plan was intended to reflect the changing economic and environmental conditions in the Tahoe Basin, incorporating changes to regulatory ordinances and policies that aim to promote sustainable development in the Tahoe Basin. Many environmental aspects of the Regional Plan were not changed. However, TRPA has added provisions and exemptions to encourage environmentally based renovation of buildings and the establishment of city centers. The updated Plan includes provisions that provide additional development rights to property owners who transfer their development in sensitive areas to town centers; eliminate existing barriers to environmental redevelopment of older buildings; expand land coverage exemptions for pervious construction and alternative transportation roadways; simplify the permitting process for homeowners into one process that meets local, state, regional, and federal requirements; and add incentives for completing BMPs.[95] In addition, the updated Plan allows for the development of an additional 3,200 residential units and 200,000 square feet for commercial use. The updated Plan also incorporates new standards and goals from the 2011 TMDL and the 2012 Regional Transportation Plan (Mobility 2035).[96]

Some environmental groups have criticized these updates, stating that TRPA is placing development and business interests over the environment. Sierra Club and the local advocacy group, Friends of the West Shore, have filed suit against TRPA, claiming that their members will suffer irreparable injury as a result of the update and that TRPA has failed to comply with the Bi- Compact of 1969.[97] Others—including the environmental non-profit League to Save Lake Tahoe—believe the revisions to the Regional Plan will allow the Plan to adapt to and address stakeholder interests, concerns, and conditions that have surfaced in the Basin since 1987.[98] For example, resort associations in the Tahoe Basin state that TRPA's old policies were unnecessarily strict and inconsistent, which stifled investment in the area.[99] In addition, TRPA argues that the update will lead to the transfer of development into city centers and out of sensitive lands, reducing automobile use and urban runoff.[100]

Complementary to the Regional Plan update, TRPA created seven new priority programs for the Tahoe Basin based on the 2011 Threshold Evaluation assessment: Stormwater Management Program; Watershed Management Program; Invasive Species Program; Forest Ecosystem and Hazardous Fuels Reduction Program; Scenic Program; Air Quality and Transportation Program; and Threatened, Endangered, and Sensitive Species Program. The federal government may have a role in each of these programs. Improving water clarity through watershed and stormwater management may be used to meet the "Clarity Challenge" included in the CWA Section 208 Water Management Plan.[101] Further, FWS might broaden its Aquatic Invasive Species program to address invasive species issues in the Basin and coordinate with nonfederal entities to conserve threatened and endangered species listed under ESA. In addition, USGS may have an increased role in the Tahoe Basin, working with participating universities to provide the best available science to guide restoration efforts and adapt for possible climate variability.[102]

Issues for Congress

The federal role in restoring the Tahoe Basin is significant. Congress has supported this role through legislation that authorizes funding for federal participation in restoration activities in the Basin. Congress might consider retaining the existing federal role in restoration or expanding this role. Some have suggested that Congress could authorize and appropriate additional funds for implementing the EIP and other restoration efforts, conduct oversight of the development of federal projects in the Basin, or assist in the creation and implementation of an adaptive management plan for restoration.[103] Some in Congress have defined the next steps for federal involvement in restoring the Basin by introducing legislation in the 113th Congress. S. 1451 would reauthorize funding for restoring the Basin, expand the ability of federal agencies to work with state and local governments on restoration, and authorize federal support for public outreach and science programs in the Basin. (See box below for more details.)

LAKE TAHOE RESTORATION ACT OF 2013

S. 1451, the Lake Tahoe Restoration Act of 2013, would reauthorize funding for environmental restoration and forest management activities in the Tahoe Basin and amend the Lake Tahoe Restoration Act of 2000. In comparison to existing law, S. 1451 would broaden the role of the federal government to include the funding, planning, and implementing of new environment restoration activities; managing land; supporting local government efforts in restoration, stormwater management, fire risk reduction, and forest management; collaborating with agencies and the science community to implement measures to objectively evaluate restoration activities and to provide objective information to guide decision-making; and conducting public education and outreach programs. The act authorizes $415 million over the next 10 fiscal years. This includes, among others, an authorization for $75 million to the Secretary of Agriculture (Secretary) or the Administrator of the EPA (Administrator) for stormwater management, $38 million to the Secretary or the Assistant Secretary of the Army Corps (Assistant Secretary) or for grants by the Administrator for Upper Truckee River restoration projects, $135 million to the Secretary for fuel reduction and forest management, $30 million to the Director of the FWS (Director) for the Aquatic Invasive Species Program, $20 million to the Director for the Lahontan Cutthroat Trout Recovery Program, and $30 million to the Chief of the Forest Service for the Lake Tahoe Basin Science Program. This act includes cost sharing measures. The states of California and Nevada are to pay for half of the costs for authorized projects. Local governments are to pay a quarter of costs for fire risk and forest management projects. In addition, the U.S. Army Corps of Engineers can enter into agreements with nonfederal interests and provide funds for technical assistance at a federal share of project costs of 65%. The act also includes criteria for development of a prioritized list of all EIP projects to be presented to Congress and revised at least every two years. The Secretary, Administrator, and the Directors of FWS and USGS are also tasked with collaborating with TRPA and conducting public education and outreach programs. In particular, the Director of USGS would provide scientific and technical guidance for all approved programs. In addition, the annual budget would include an interagency crosscut budget and detailed accounting of received and obligated funding to achieve EIP goals for the preceding year.

Congress might also consider addressing other prevalent issues in the Basin such as changing weather patterns and their effect on the ecosystem and the economy, the status and source of federal funding for restoration, what constitutes sustainable development in the Basin and how that affects the restoration of the ecosystem, overseeing and analyzing progress in restoration, and whether restoration efforts are having an impact.

Funding

Federal funding for restoration in the Tahoe Basin has come largely from mandatory funds provided under SNPLMA. As of FY2012, this funding was exhausted. Based on cost-share estimates, some might contend that the federal government is still responsible for providing an additional $480 million for restoration activities under the 2008-2018 EIP. Some question whether the federal government will be able to continue to fund restoration in the Tahoe Basin at historical levels in the current fiscal climate.[104] If funding is reduced by the federal government, it is unclear if other parties will increase funding to meet restoration needs or decrease their funding to meet cost-share requirements under LTRA of 2000. If funding is decreased by all parties, some stakeholders are concerned that restoration efforts may decline or that restoration gains may be reversed.[105]

Currently, federal funding for EIP projects is provided separately for each of the federal departments involved (DOD, DOI, USDA, EPA, DOT). Funding for hazardous fuel reduction and wildfire prevention activities and projects authorized under LTRA is authorized through SNPLMA. The Secretary of the Interior has discretion on how to manage these funds and is authorized to transfer funds to the Secretary of Agriculture or another Secretary if a funding agreement is signed. SNPLMA authorizes the Secretary to direct funding for the EIP "in an amount equal to the cumulative amounts authorized to be appropriated for such projects under such acts [referring to Lake Tahoe Restoration Act]."[106] Therefore, if the authorization for appropriations is expired under LTRA, it is uncertain if SNPLMA funds can be used for the EIP. Funding restoration projects under SNPLMA might require an amendment to SNPLMA to authorize funding directly (i.e., without having to reauthorize LTRA) or reauthorizing appropriations under LTRA. In addition, some question whether revenue from land sales would cover the authorized amount in the proposed legislation. SNPLMA authorized the disposal of up to 74,000 acres of federal land; only 28,791 acres remain to be sold as of July 31, 2013.[107] With approximately only one-quarter of land remaining to be sold and a declining average price per acre, it is unclear whether $415 million could be appropriated from SNPLMA to be used toward Lake Tahoe restoration. Nevertheless, if funds for restoration activities cannot be procured under SNPLMA, restoration activities could receive discretionary funding from Congress.

Proposed legislation by Congress would address this funding dilemma by reauthorizing funding for restoration activities in the Tahoe Basin. S. 1451 would authorize $415 million in appropriations for restoration projects in the Tahoe Basin for a period of 10 years. These projects would aim to address water clarity, forest health, invasive species, and science research, among other things.[108]

Nonfederal stakeholders are contemplating alternative sources of funding for restoration. For example, TRPA is contemplating using public-private partnerships[109] for generating funds and using proceeds from the Tahoe Fund for restoration.[110]

Views on Progress

Whether or not restoration in the Tahoe Basin has been implemented to receive the "biggest bang for the buck" remains controversial. Some local groups argue that little progress has been made despite the $1.7 billion provided for restoration.[111] Local groups have cited several reasons for lack of progress, including the use of ineffective technologies and management practices, a disproportionate amount of monitoring and planning activities, and the weakening of environmental protection and standards over time.[112] Despite these criticisms, these stakeholders still support funding restoration with changes in how restoration is managed. However, according to TRPA, current efforts represent the best management practices given the science information available.[113] TRPA states that restoration efforts and monitoring have contributed to significant environmental improvements despite variations in weather and unforeseen circumstances that could have damaged the ecosystem.[114] Scientific uncertainty about the impacts of changing precipitation patterns and warming temperatures on the environment makes it challenging to quantify the benefits or progress from particular restoration activities.[115]

Some local groups contend that current restoration approaches in the Tahoe Basin are ineffective in restoring the ecosystem.[116] For example, the Tahoe Pipe Club contends that the watershed management practices used by TRPA do not adequately address runoff that enters the lake. They further note that ineffective management practices could significantly contribute to the decline in water quality during summer months. This issue is further exacerbated by the fact that half of EIP funding goes toward water quality and stormwater management projects. Other stakeholders, however, cite that improving annual and winter water clarity are signs that water management strategies are leading to progress.[117] They state that there are multiple factors which affect water quality that are outside of the scope of restoration, such as changes in precipitation patterns and water temperatures. Stakeholders contend that the measures in place have prevented greater environmental decline from these outside factors.[118]

In addition, in public comment documents, individual citizens contended that restoration funds are inefficiently distributed, which has hampered progress.[119] Some residents contend that too much of the funding goes toward monitoring and assessment plans and activities which don't contribute to actual restoration.[120] Further, they contend that TRPA and other agencies involved in restoration should require proof that a project will have tangible environmental benefits before funding is provided. However, other stakeholders contend that monitoring and assessment activities contribute by informing future decision-making.[121] Scientists have been continuously monitoring Lake Tahoe since 1968, and they state these long-term data provide insight into management practices that work in the Tahoe Basin by allowing stakeholders to measure progress of restoration over time. TRPA also states that monitoring may become more important as agencies and stakeholders consider new measures to address the changing climate.[122]

Congress may consider conducting oversight on restoration and progress in the Basin. Several policies used by other large-scale ecosystem restoration initiatives could be applied to the Tahoe Basin and EIP. For example, crosscut budgets could be used to organize and identify restoration projects, and their funding and status on an annual basis. These types of budgets are used in restoration initiatives in the Everglades and the Great Lakes. Further, Congress could authorize an independent entity to review progress and issues associated with restoration in the Tahoe Basin. For example, restoration in the Everglades and in some selected cases in the California Bay-Delta is analyzed and reviewed by the National Research Council (NRC). NRC conducts independent reviews of the scientific and some policy factors in these restoration initiatives. S. 1451 would attempt to address this issue by requiring federal agencies to present Congress with an annual report that contains a crosscut budget and detailed accounting of received and obligated funding to achieve EIP goals.

Balancing Restoration and the Economy

There is growing controversy between environmental and development interests in the Tahoe Basin.[123] Some local business associations contend that limits on development derived from the Regional Plan are inhibiting economic growth in the Basin.[124] The Tahoe Basin economy relies in part on the preservation of the environment; growth of the economy may require both additional development and improved environmental health of the Basin, according to TRPA.[125] Due to the connection between recreation, tourism, development, and the environment, some contend that sustainable development in the region is warranted. Some environmental groups, however, contend that limits on development have led to significant environmental gains in the Basin, and are necessary for maintaining progress in restoration.[126] This controversy is being addressed at the state level through negotiations between Nevada and California. Specifically, Nevada contends that permitting processes and limits on development have led to the decline of economic growth in the Basin, in particular the gaming industry.[127] To address this issue, the Nevada legislature passed a law (SB 271) in 2011 that required the state to leave the Bi-State Compact in 2015 unless the Compact is amended to consider economic conditions and the effect of environmental regulations on the economy when making decisions on development. This law was repealed in 2013 as a result of negotiations between California and Nevada.[128] Changes made to the Regional Plan in 2012 were also made, in part, in response to Nevada concerns about development.[129] Negotiations between California and Nevada resulted in certain agreements that addressed amending the Compact. The agreement included two potential amendments to the Compact. Generally, the agreement included that:

- The Regional Plan should reflect changing economic conditions in the Basin and the economic effect of regulations on commerce; and
- Any party that brings litigation against the Regional Plan or TRPA has to have a higher burden of proof that the Regional Plan is not in conformance with the Compact.

The next step in this process would be for the states of California and Nevada to define changes to the Compact in state law.[130] Any changes to the Compact approved by the states would then become proposed changes to the Compact. Any changes to the Compact would require congressional approval.

Updates to the Regional Plan in 2012 that allow for additional development and increased local control of development have led to litigation.[131] If the Regional Plan is struck down, some contend that Nevada will leave the Bi-State Compact. This could result in TRPA being dissolved and two regional planning agencies being created, one for managing development on the California side of the Basin and one for managing development on the Nevada side. If this happens, the federal role in restoration and collaboration with TRPA and EIP would be unclear. The current controversy could be addressed by Congress through oversight or legislation.

Climate Change

Changing weather patterns in the Tahoe Basin may have adverse impacts on the Tahoe Basin ecosystem and ongoing restoration and management efforts. Scientists have noted significant trends of warming temperatures in the past century, especially in the past two decades. For example, since 1910, average air temperatures have increased by approximately four degrees Fahrenheit, and since 1970, the average lake water temperature has increased by around one degree Fahrenheit.[132] Changes in weather and increased weather variability have raised concerns about the future environmental and economic health of the Tahoe Basin. In response to these concerns, stakeholders have begun to formulate Basin-wide strategies to address climate change. Further, the state of California has done surveys to estimate the economic effects of climate change in the Tahoe Basin. In addition to these efforts, some contend that more resources should be directed towards scientific research and adaptive management of restoration in the Tahoe Basin.

Scientists have predicted that changes in weather and increased weather variability in the Tahoe Basin may have negative impacts on the ecosystem.[133] For example, an increase in winter flooding (e.g., caused by earlier snowmelt and increased winter rains) may lead to a decline in water quality due to higher levels of urban runoff and debris entering the lake.[134] Further, scientists have expressed concern that hotter summers may lead to higher levels of drought, thereby increasing the risk of wildfires.[135] Additionally, many of the Tahoe Basin's invasive species originate in warmer waters than Lake Tahoe.[136] Therefore, increased water temperatures may help non-native species out-compete native species. Water quality may also decrease due to physical changes in water circulation brought on by climate variability. Lake Tahoe, like many lakes, stratifies into distinct thermal layers of water. Seasonal changes promote the mixing of these distinct layers, which allows for oxygen and other nutrients to spread throughout the lake's water column. Warmer temperatures in the Tahoe Basin have, in part, extended the lake's period of stratification, which may reduce the depth to which water mixes.[137] For example, in 2012, the bottom waters mixed to a depth of 820 feet, as compared to 2011 when mixing occurred at a depth of around 1,430 feet.[138] Some researchers are concerned that the reduced mixing time may lead to complete anoxia of bottom waters later in the century.[139] The impacts from these changes could have long-lasting effects on the trophic structure and ecosystem of the Basin.

Changing weather patterns in the Basin may lead to changes in restoration strategies. For example, increased wildfire risk may require USFS to modify its Forest Management Plan[140] to include a stronger emphasis on hazardous fuels reduction and tree thinning activities. Changes in water quality might require changes in regulatory actions under the CWA (e.g., changes in strategies for achieving TMDLs).

Congress could address this issue by authorizing additional funds for scientific and adaptive management efforts within the Tahoe Basin. Congress could also authorize increased federal participation in efforts to create new or adaptive strategies to address climate change in the Basin. Under S. 1451, $30 million would be authorized for the Forest Service to develop and implement, in coordination with the Tahoe Science Consortium, the Lake Tahoe Basin Science Program (Science Program).[141] The Science Program would develop and regularly update integrated multiagency programmatic monitoring and assessment plans to measure and evaluate progress and assess the risks and impacts of changing weather patterns. In addition, the Science Program would provide scientific and technical support for the development of appropriate management strategies that accommodate changing weather and precipitation in the Tahoe Basin.[142]

CONCLUSION

The Lake Tahoe Basin is considered by some to be an area of national significance and is recognized by the EPA as an "Outstanding National Resource Water" under the federal Clean Water Act. The Basin provides both recreational and environmental services and is tied to the regional economy. Over the years, development in the Basin has led to alterations in its ecosystem. This has prompted federal, state, local, and private efforts to conduct restoration. Since 1997 restoration efforts among stakeholders have been largely organized under the EIP. Many use this date to evaluate progress in restoration.

Some contend that significant restoration progress has been made in the Basin since 1997.[143] They cite the recent threshold evaluations, which indicate that more than half of the studied environmental indicators established in the 1980s have been reached. They note that more than 500 restoration projects have been completed or are ongoing, contributing to more than 50,000 acres of treated or restored lands, 400 miles of treated roads, and 15,000 acres of restored wildlife habitat. While progress in restoration has been reported, some environmental concerns remain. Lake Tahoe faces continued water pollution that has contributed to a loss of a third of its water clarity in the past 40 years. While annual clarity is stabilizing and winter clarity is showing trends of improvement, it is expected to take until 2077 for the lake to return to its historical clarity, according to TMDL. Further, while efforts to reduce fuel loads have been implemented, some suggest that it will take decades before forests return to a healthy state.[144] Additionally, while there have been improvements in the air quality of the Basin, efforts to curb automobile use in the area continue. Sensitive and listed species' populations show signs of stability or improvement, but invasive species continue to threaten native species populations. Future restoration activities in the Basin may address water quality, invasive species, climate change adaptation, land use, and forest management.

The federal government has played a significant role in restoring the Basin ecosystem. It is unclear how this role might evolve due to changes in federal funding and state actions centering on potential changes to the Compact. Federal involvement will continue through efforts under laws such as the LTRA 2000, CWA, CAA, and ESA. Further, proposed legislation such as S. 1451 could expand federal collaboration and participation with nonfederal stakeholders in restoration efforts and reauthorize federal funding for implementing restoration projects and activities.

APPENDIX. CHRONOLOGY OF LAKE TAHOE BASIN

2 million-3 million Years Ago	Lake Tahoe Basin and Lake Tahoe are formed.
10,000 Years Ago	First appearance of nomadic groups in the Tahoe Basin. These nomads were the ancestors of the current Washoe, Maidu, and Paiute Indian Tribes.

1844	John C. Fremont is the first American to sight Lake Tahoe. He was leading expedition parties on the Oregon Trail and into the Sierra Nevadas.
1852	The first permanent American settlement is established in the Tahoe Basin.
1859	The Comstock Lode is discovered in nearby Virginia City. Over 20,000 prospectors move to Virginia City to mine for silver and gold.
1860s-1890s	To accommodate the growing number of settlers in the area, the Tahoe Basin forests are cut for timber and fuel. This becomes known as the "Comstock Era."
1864	Tahoe City founded as a resort community for Virginia City residents.
1880	4,000-foot tramway completed for carrying lumber. By 1896, when the lumber flume was shut down, over 60% of the mature trees in the forest had been cut down since operation began in 1880.
1887	The Mackinaw (lake) trout is introduced in Lake Tahoe for sport-fishing purposes.
1889	The California Legislature passes an anti-sawdust statue preventing mills from dumping sawdust into Truckee River. The Nevada Legislature had passed resolutions calling for California to prevent dumping as early as 1869.
1899	The Lake Tahoe Forest Reserve is created by the federal government. It covers 136,000 acres of forest in the Tahoe Basin. First attempt in Congress to make Lake Tahoe a National Park. There were subsequent efforts in 1913, 1930, and 1935. All efforts failed, reportedly due to the environmental degradation from development in the area.
1911	The U.S. Forest Service builds its first station in the Tahoe Basin.
1920	By 1920, the USFS own 25% of all Tahoe Basin land.
1927	First state park created in the Tahoe Basin by the state of California. The state of California now manages three parks and a recreation area in the Tahoe Basin.
1931	Nevada legalizes gaming. 5,000 tourists from California visit Nevada in the first week.
1938-1944	The Pyramid Lake cutthroat trout, once the largest and most plentiful fish in the Basin, officially becomes extinct due to overfishing and water diversions. Its cousin, the native Lahontan cutthroat trout, is purposefully reintroduced into the area for fishing.
1949	Both the California and Nevada Legislatures pass laws prohibiting disposal of waste into Lake Tahoe or within 100 feet of tributaries. Nevada also begins to require permits for new construction that will involve discharge of waste in those areas.

(Continued)

1955	California and Nevada form the California-Nevada Interstate Compact Commission to respond to interstate issues concerning Lake Tahoe and Truckee River. This commission is active until the creation of TRPA by the Bi-State Compact in 1969.
1958	Sand Harbor State Park becomes the first Nevada state park in the Tahoe Basin. Incorporated into the larger Lake Tahoe Nevada State Park in 1967.
1959	The University of California, Davis, begins scientific research on Lake Tahoe. This becomes the Tahoe Environmental Research Center.
1960	Neighboring Squaw Valley holds the 1960 Winter Olympics.
1962	The first secchi disc reading is done in Lake Tahoe. Clarity measured at 136 feet.
1965-1980	The USFS begins a policy to acquire all available parcels of land in the Tahoe Basin. Purchases over 36,000 acres over the next 15 years.
1965	The state of California and the state of Nevada create a joint study commission to investigate worsening environmental problems in the Tahoe Basin.
1969	The Bi-State Compact is ratified by Congress. TRPA is formed.
1970	The Lahontan Cutthroat trout is listed as endangered under the Endangered Species Conservation Act of 1969 (replaced by the ESA in 1972).
1975	The Lahontan Cutthroat trout is downgraded to threatened under the ESA due to hatchery success.
1976	More than 70% of the Basin is publicly owned.
1980	On December 19, the Bi-State Compact is amended to include the development of a regional plan and environmental thresholds, among other things.
1980	The Santini-Burton Act (P.L. 96-586) is passed. This authorized the USFS to acquire environmentally sensitive lands, restore watershed on federal forest lands, and administer erosion control grants to local government. To date over 13,000 acres have been purchased under this act.
1981	The first moratorium on development in the Tahoe Basin goes into effect on August 24 until August 26, 1983.
1982	The environmental thresholds are adopted by TRPA in August.
1983	The second moratorium on development in the Tahoe Basin goes into effect until April 25, 1984. It is considered more restrictive than the earlier version.
1984	The first (1984) Regional Plan is adopted. However, that same day the state of California placed an injunction on the Plan on the grounds that it is not stringent enough to protect the Basin.

1987	After litigation and negotiations, the completely revised 1987 Regional Plan is successfully adopted.
1996	The Bureau of Land Management finalizes a land exchange of 1,400 acres of Las Vegas land for 35 acres of Lake Tahoe property. The 35 acres are given to USFS.
	Nevada and California voters approve $30 million for erosion control and stream restoration in Tahoe Basin.
1997	President Clinton holds the Lake Tahoe Presidential Forum. Under Executive Order 13507, the Lake Tahoe Federal Interagency Partnership and the Environmental Improvement Program (EIP) are created to assist with meeting the Regional Plan.
2000	The Lake Tahoe Restoration Act of 2000 (P.L. 106-506) is signed, authorizing $300 million for EIP restoration projects.
2003	The Southern Nevada Public Lands Management Act (SNPLMA; P.L. 105-263) is amended, appropriating $300 million towards EIP restoration projects.
2006	SNPLMA is amended to include funding for a "Hazardous Fuels Reduction and Treatment Program."
2007	The Angora Wildfire burns 3,100 acres in the Tahoe Basin, destroying 254 residences and 75 commercial structures, damaging another 35 residences, and injuring 3 people.
2008	The Aquatic Invasive Species Program is created.
2008	The EIP is updated by TRPA to guide the second decade of the capital improvement program.
2009	Lahontan Cutthroat Trout recovery begins.
2011	The final TMDL is approved by the EPA for Lake Tahoe. The TMDL sets the clarity standard for the lake at 97 feet.
2012	The Regional Plan is updated for the first time since 1987. The update becomes effective in 2013.
2012	SNPLMA finishes its $300 million dollar funding commitment towards Lake Tahoe restoration.

End Notes

[1] North Lake Tahoe Visitors' Bureau, *Forest and Wildlife*, http://www.gotahoenorth.com/about-tahoe/environment/ forest-and-wildlife.

[2] Tahoe Regional Planning Agency, *Environmental Improvement Program Highlights and Accomplishment*, August 2011. http://www.trpa.org/wp-content/uploads/EIP_4PG_2011_FNL.pdf. (Hereinafter *TRPA EIP Highlights*.)

[3] California Regional Water Quality Control Board, Lahontan Region and the Nevada Division of Environmental Protection, *Final Lake Tahoe Total Maximum Daily Load*, Carson City, NV, August 2011. p. 2-2. (Hereinafter *Water Board and NDEP TMDL*.)

[4] Lake Tahoe Basin Management Unit, U.S. Department of Agriculture, *Trees in Transition*, http://www.fs.usda.gov/ detail/ltbmu/learning/?cid=stelprdb5109573. (Hereinafter referred to as *Trees in Transition*.)

[5] Water clarity is measured by lowering a Secchi disk into the water to the depth at which it is no longer visible. *Water Board and NDEP TMDL*, p. 4-1.

[6] Holdings overseen by USDA Lake Tahoe Basin Management Unit. Website is at http://www.fs.usda.gov.

[7] *TRPA EIP Highlights*.

[8] See http://www.gpo.gov/fdsys/pkg/FR-1997-08-01/pdf/97-20497.pdf for the complete Executive Order 13057.

[9] SNPLMA directs revenue from BLM land sales in Carson County (which includes Las Vegas) towards the general education fund (5% of revenue), the Southern Nevada Water Authority (10%), and environmental programs chosen at the discretion of the Secretary Interior (85%). This funding can be made available for Lake Tahoe Restoration Projects and Hazardous Fuels Reduction and Wildfire Prevention (which apply to the Tahoe Basin forests), among other programs. See http://www.blm.gov/pgdata/content/nv/en/snplma.html for more.

[10] USGS, Lake Tahoe Data Clearinghouse, December 2012. Available at http://tahoe.usgs.gov/.

[11] Lake Tahoe is one of the 20 oldest lakes in the world. See http://terc.ucdavis.edu/documents/ DocentManual_Chap4_ScienceAndResearch.pdf.

[12] Lake Tahoe was given this designation in 1980. It is one of only three water bodies in the western United States to be considered an ONRW. *Water Board and NDEP TMDL*, p.1-1.

[13] ONRW is given the highest level of protection under Tier 3 of the State's anti-degradation policy. Water quality must be "maintained and protected." Proposed new or expansion of existing point sources is prohibited (this applies to any point sources upstream that will have adverse impacts on the ONRW). For more, see the EPA's Water Quality Standards Handbook, Chapter 4, Section 7 (40 C.F.R. 131.12(a)(3). Online at http://water.epa.gov/ scitech/swguidance/standards/handbook/chapter04.cfm#section5.

[14] USGS, Lake Tahoe Data Clearinghouse, December 2012. Found at http://tahoe.usgs.gov/.

[15] See Bureau of Reclamation for details on Lake Tahoe Dam, http://www.usbr.gov/projects/ Facility.jsp?fac_Name= Lake+Tahoe+Dam&groupName=Overview.

[16] Tahoe Regional Planning Agency, *2011 Threshold Evaluation*, Final Draft, December 12, 2012, http://www.trpa.org/ regional-plan/threshold-evaluation/. (Hereinafter known as *TRPA Threshold Evaluation*.)

[17] Calculated from the Fish and Wildlife Service website (http://www.fws.gov/endangered/) and USDA Rare Plant and Fungi Survey 2010. Federally listed species under the Endangered Species Act (16 U.S.C. §§1531-1543) include the Lahontan cutthroat trout, mountain beaver, mountain yellow-legged frog, and red-legged frog.

[18] For example, see FWS's documents and plans concerning the Lahontan cutthroat trout at http://ecos.fws.gov/ speciesProfile/profile/speciesProfile.action?spcode=E00Y.

[19] *Water Board and NDEP TMDL*, p. 5-7.

[20] University of Rhode Island, "Understanding Lake Ecology," http://www.uri.edu/cels/nrs/whl/ Teaching/361-10/ 3_Receiving_Waters/Understand_Lake_Ecology.pdf.

[21] See Robert Coats, Joaquim Perez-Losada, and Geoffrey Schladow et al., "The Warming of Lake Tahoe," *Climate Change*, vol. 76 (2006), p. 121-148.

[22] Environmental Protection Agency, *National Lakes Assessment: A Collaborative Survey of the Nation's Lakes*, EPA 841-R-09-001, April 2010, http://www.epa.gov/owow/LAKES/ lakessurvey/pdf/nla_chapter5.pdf.

[23] UC Davis Tahoe Environmental Research Center, *State of the Lake Report 2012*, Incline Village, NV, http://terc.ucdavis.edu/stateofthelake/historic.html. (Hereinafter known as *TERC State of the Lake 2012*.)

[24] Environmental Protection Agency, *National Lakes Assessment: A Collaborative Survey of the Nation's Lakes*, EPA 841-R-09-001, April 2010.

[25] Clarity readings in Lake Tahoe began in 1962.

[26] UC Davis Tahoe Environmental Research Center, *State of the Lake Report 2013*, Incline Village, NV, http://terc.ucdavis.edu/stateofthelake/. (Hereinafter known as *TERC State of the Lake 2013.*)

[27] *TERC State of the Lake 2012*, Section 9.1.

[28] For more on CWA and TMDL designation see CRS Report R42752, *Clean Water Act and Pollutant Total Maximum Daily Loads (TMDLs)*, by Claudia Copeland.

[29] Estimated fine particle, phosphorous, and nitrogen loads must be reduced by 65%, 35%, and 10% respectively under the TMDL.

[30] *TERC State of the Lake 2012*, Section 9.1.

[31] This standard was the average annual secchi depth from 1967 to 1971.

[32] *Water Board and NDEP TMDL*, p. ES-3.

[33] Lake Tahoe Basin Management Unit, U.S. Department of Agriculture, *Trees in Transition*, http://www.fs.usda.gov/ detail/ltbmu/learning/?cid=stelprdb5109573. (Hereinafter referred to as *Trees in Transition.*)

[34] *Trees in Transition.*

[35] *Trees in Transition.*

[36] *Trees in Transition.*

[37] Autumn Bernstein and Joan Clayburgh, *Dangerous Development: Wildfire and Rural Sprawl in the Sierra Nevada*, Sierra Nevada Alliance, September 18, 2007, http://www.sierranevadaalliance.org/news/newsreleases/profile.shtml? index=1190123635_28156&cat =&loc=&listpage=1.

[38] The last fire occurred in 2007 and was known as the Angora Fire. Economic data provided by "Reflections of Angora Fire 5 Years After the Devastation," *Lake Tahoe News*, June 2, 2012, and Cal Fire at http://cdfdata.fire.ca.gov/ incidents/incidents_details_info?incident_id =184.

[39] *TERC State of the Lake 2012,* Section 6.11.

[40] U.S. Army Corps of Engineers, *Lake Tahoe Region Aquatic Invasive Species Management Plan, California-Nevada*, September 2009, http://anstaskforce.gov/State Plans/Lake_ Tahoe_Region_AIS_Management_Plan.pdf.

[41] Ibid.

[42] For example, predation by the introduced mysid shrimp has been attributed to the elimination or near elimination of three small crustaceans. Ibid.

[43] Ibid.

[44] Economic impacts considered were losses to recreation value, tourism spending, property values, and increase boat/pier maintenance. Ibid.

[45] *TERC State of the Lake 2012.* Section 6.5-6.7.

[46] *TERC State of the Lake 2012.* Section 6.5-6.7.

[47] National Invasive Species Council, *Prevention*, http://www.invasivespecies.gov/global/ prevention/prevention_index.html.

[48] U.S. Army Corps of Engineers, *Lake Tahoe Region Aquatic Invasive Species Management Plan, California-Nevada.* September 2009, http://anstaskforce.gov/State%20Plans/ Lake_Tahoe_Region_AIS_Management_Plan.pdf.

[49] Environmental design refers to planning and design features included in development to address environmental surroundings. This includes reducing impervious land coverage (maintaining open space), installing water savings and management technology, energy efficiency measures, and using native plants and grasses for landscaping. Joanne Marchetta (Executive Director at TRPA), "Funding Will Be Tahoe's Next Major Challenge," *Lake Tahoe News*, June 19, 2013.

[50] Although the air quality in the Basin is no longer an issue, the Basin was in non-attainment for CO in the 1990s from car exhaust. A CO Maintenance Plan was created in 1998 which required that attainment was maintained for the next 20 years. Thus, Lake Tahoe will be monitored until 2018 for CO.

[51] These include county governments and their respective utility districts, the Washoe tribe, North Lake Tahoe Resort Association, Lake Tahoe Gaming Alliance, and the League to Save Lake Tahoe, among others. Full list can be found on p. 29 of the Tahoe Regional Planning Agency. *Restoration in Progress: Environmental Improvement Program Update*, 2010, http://www.trpa.org/wp-content/uploads/EIP_Report_Update.pdf. (Hereinafter known as *TRPA EIP Update*.)

[52] The original compact was P.L. 91-148. It has since been amended. The current form can be found at http://www.trpa.org/wp-content/uploads/Bistate_Compact.pdf.

[53] The thresholds also indirectly define the amount of additional land development that can occur. TRPA must ensure that any new development will not lead to non-attainment of the thresholds.

[54] Tahoe Regional Planning Agency, *Threshold Carrying Capacities*, first released 1982 and last amended in 2012, http://www.trpa.org/wp-content/uploads/Resolution-82-11_12-2012.pdf.

[55] Contact Information can be found at http://www.trpa.org/about-trpa/governing-board/.

[56] This includes litigation and enforcement decisions; directing legal counsel; budget, personnel, and contract matters; other administrative actions concerning meetings, committees, and staff. More information available in TRPA's Rules of Procedure, available at http://www.trpa.org/wp-content/uploads/TRPA_Rules_of_Procedure1.pdf.

[57] The Commission includes representatives from USFS and the Natural Resources Conservation Service, which is within the Department of the Interior. Currently, two seats are vacant (one from the Air Resources Board and another from the Washoe Tribe). Contact information available at http://www.trpa.org/about-trpa/advisory-planning-commission/.

[58] TRPA is one of the few Metropolitan Planning Organizations (MPO) with land use power. TRPA has the authority to regulate growth and development by setting standards for zoning, subdivisions, waste and sewage disposal, piers, buildings, outdoor advertising, mobile-home parks, house relocation, air and water pollution, watershed protection, and soil and sedimentation control, among others.

[59] Documents available under the "What is the Regional Plan?" heading at http://www.trpa.org/regional-plan/.

[60] Derek Kauneckis, Leslie Koziol, and Mark Imperial, "Tahoe Regional Planning Agency: The Evolution of Collaboration" (Grant from the National Academy of Public Administration, Indiana University, School of Public and Environmental Affairs, 2000), http://people.uncw.edu/imperialm/ Instructor/Papers/NAPA_TRPA_Case.pdf.

[61] Until the Regional Plan Update in 2012, Thresholds were evaluated every five years.

[62] Telephone communication between CRS and TRPA, August 7, 2013.

[63] The current list applies for January 1, 2012 to December 31, 2016. In total, there are 530 projects recognized. The list is available at http://www.trpa.org/wp-content/uploads/EIP_5-Year_List-2012_through_20162.pdf.

[64] *TRPA EIP Update*.

[65] See the *TRPA EIP Update* for description, potential programs, and needs for each focus area.

[66] Tahoe Fund, "Tahoe Fund Supports New Federal Lake Tahoe Restoration Act," press release, August 1, 2013, http://www.tahoefund.org/media/tahoe-fund-supports-new-federal-lake-tahoe-restoration-act/.

[67] *TRPA EIP Update*.

[68] The federal government is involved with 305 separate projects as of 2013. 223 projects have a federal agency assigned as an implementer of the project; 184 projects receive at least partial funding from the federal government.

[69] See Executive Order 13057, http://www.gpo.gov/fdsys/pkg/FR-1997-08-01/pdf/97-20497.pdf.

[70] Lake Tahoe Federal Interagency Partnership, *A Federal Vision for the Environmental Improvement Program at Lake Tahoe*, June 6, 2006, http://www.fs.usda.gov/Internet/FSE_DOCUMENTS/fsm9_046280.pdf.

[71] Ibid.

[72] TRPA is currently revisiting this number due to unforeseen stakeholder fiscal constraints (requested funding numbers established before the 2008 economic decline). Telephone communication between CRS and TRPA, August 7, 2013.

[73] This funding included $10 million a year to be equally matched by the state and local governments through an Erosion Control Grants Program.

[74] Proceeds go towards environmental improvement, general education fund, and the Southern Nevada water authority. Federal holdings are under the Department of the Interior's Bureau of Land Management.

[75] This amendment was known as the 'White Pine Amendment.' Lake Tahoe is one of three areas that receive funds from this category. Proposals are directly submitted through the Nevada SNPLMA process, not the Lake Tahoe process.

[76] This refers to activities necessary to achieve an agency's missions and goals. These activities may result in environmental improvements, but are not considered EIP projects as defined by TRPA.

[77] *Water Board and NDEP TMDL*, p. ES-2.

[78] BMPs for homeowners may include planting native vegetation, reducing irrigation use, installing parking barriers, replacing dirt driveways with paved driveways, or adding gravel under roof drip-lines. All homes in the Tahoe Basin are required to have BMPs installed. Tahoe Regional Planning Agency, *Appendix IE-3- Stormwater Management/BMP Retrofit Program Overview*, 2011, http://www.trpa.org/wp-content/uploads/11_AppxIE-3_TRPAStormwater_FINAL.pdf.

[79] The Basin was in non-attainment for CO until 1996. The maintenance plan for attainment will be in effect until 2018.

[80] Moving Ahead for Progress in the 21st Century Act (MAP-21) requires TRPA (as a MPO) to develop a long range transportation map. In addition, the Bi-State Compact requires that a Regional Transportation Plan be maintained. SB 375 passed by California requires TMPO to develop a sustainable community's strategy, which will reduce greenhouse gas emissions per person by 12% in 2020 and by 7% in 2035 (the figure is lower in 2035 due to population forecasts and economic recovery).

[81] The actual transportation plan can be found at http://tahoempo.org/Mobility2035/.

[82] Includes U.S. Hwy 50. Currently, the U.S. Hwy 50 traffic threshold has been reached. The threshold is set at 7% below 1981 traffic. In 2011, traffic volume was 22% lower than in 1981.

[83] For example, the Mountain Yellow-Legged Frog has a recovery plan that addresses all California populations.

[84] More information on the AIS program can be found at http://www.fws.gov/nevada/nv_species/invasive_species/ lt_index.htm.

[85] Dating Clearinghouse found at http://tahoe.usgs.gov/index.html.

[86] More on Tahoe Science Consortium can be found at http://tahoescience.org/.

[87] The independent review board includes seven members, representing academia and environmental consulting firms, which are considered experts in any of the following fields: air quality, water quality, recreation/tourism, wilderness management, forest health, fisheries, or wildlife.

[88] There were 151 indicators, but only 92 indicators can be quantified. Numerical standards and management standards are considered quantifiable; policy standards are not quantifiable. *TRPA Threshold Evaluation*.

[89] *TRPA Threshold Evaluation*.

[90] TERC, "Lake Tahoe Clarity the Best in 10 Years," press release, February 27, 2013.

[91] From TRPA EIP Highlights; TRPA, "Lake Tahoe EIP Marks 15 Years of Achievement," press release, August 16, 2013, http://www.trpa.org/lake-tahoe-eip-marks-15-years-of-achievement/.

[92] *TRPA Threshold Evaluation*.

[93] An example of one such local group would be the Tahoe Pipe Club. Their website is available at http://www.tahoepipeclub.com.

[94] The update to the regional plan had been originally scheduled to be passed in 2007 (20 years after the original Regional Plan had been passed). The update was enacted, in part, beginning February 2013. Some provisions are still waiting to be enacted. Kathryn Reed, "TRPA Board Approves Regional Plan Update," *Lake Tahoe News*, December 12, 2012, http://www.laketahoenews.net/2012/12/trpa-governing-board-approves-regional-plan-update/.

[95] Tahoe Regional Planning Agency, *Regional Plan Update Fact Sheet*, January 2013, http://www.trpa.org/wp-content/ uploads/RPU_FactSheet_1-15-13.pdf.

[96] For all changes, see http://www.trpa.org/wp-content/uploads/Summary_of_2012_TRPA_Code_Changes.pdf.

[97] *Sierra Club and Friends of the West Shore v. Tahoe Regional Planning Agency* (California Eastern District Court 2013). Available at http://earthjustice.org/sites/default/files/FINALTahoeRPUComplaint.pdf.

[98] Darcie Goodman-Collins, "Excited to Move Forward with Nevada on Board," *Tahoe Daily Tribune*, June 13, 2013 (Guest Column by the League to Save Lake Tahoe Executive Director).

[99] Adam Jensen, "TRPA approves Lake Tahoe Regional Plan Update, 12-1," *Tahoe Daily Tribune*, December 12, 2012. http://www.tahoedailytribune.com/article/20121212/NEWS/121219952.

[100] TRPA estimates vehicle miles traveled will be reduced by 10,000 and remove 24 acres of land coverage from sensitive lands. See http://www.trpa.org/wp-content/uploads/RPU_2pager_Numbers_3-251.pdf.

[101] This Clarity Challenge is set at 80 ft. The goal is to achieve this clarity by 2023 and maintain attainment for five years. *Water Board and NDEP TMDL*, p. 10-1.

[102] The updated EIP noted that one of the priorities was documenting and predicting effects of climate change on the Basin and management activities.

[103] For example, see League to Save Lake Tahoe, "Tahoe Leaders Applaud Restoration Bill," August 2, 2013, http://keeptahoeblue.org/news/news-main/?id=614.

[104] For example, see Tahoe Regional Planning Agency, *Strategic Plan*, February 2013, http://www.trpa.org/wp-content/ uploads/Strategic_Plan_2-4-13_web.pdf, p. 13-14. (Hereinafter *TRPA Strategic Plan*.)

[105] League to Save Lake Tahoe, "Tahoe Leaders Applaud Restoration Bill," August 2, 2013, http://keeptahoeblue.org/ news/news-main/?id=614.

[106] See Section 4(e)(3)(a)(vi) of P.L. 105-263. Note that the Fuels Reduction Program still can allocate funds above $300 million for restoration efforts related to fuels reduction in Tahoe Basin forests.

[107] The average price per acre in FY2013 was $48,480, the lowest average purchase price of any SNPLMA annual auction. Bureau of Land Management, *SNPLMA Program Statistics*, July 31, 2013, http://www.blm.gov/pgdata/etc/ medialib/blm/nv/field_offices/las_vegas_field_office/snplma/pdf/reports.Par.68547.File.dat/ 3%20PROGRAM%20STATISTICS.pdf.

[108] See the box 'Lake Tahoe Restoration Act of 2013' for more information.

[109] Public-Private Partnerships involve contract arrangements in which a nonfederal or private entity partners with the government to contribute funds, knowledge, or labor toward a project. In return, the private or nonfederal entity is guaranteed a portion of the project's revenue as repayment.

[110] The Tahoe Fund receives proceeds from specialty California and Nevada license plates, as well as donations from individuals, corporations, and foundations, which are used to help fund EIP efforts.

[111] For example, see the Tahoe Pipe Club. Anne Knowles, "With 38 Pipes Draining into Lake Tahoe Are Lake Clarity Efforts Worth a Billion Bucks?" *Lake Tahoe News*, January 17,

2012, http://www.laketahoenews.net/2012/01/with-38-pipes-draining-into-lake-tahoe-are-lake-clarity-efforts-a-fraud/.

[112] Ibid.

[113] *TRPA Strategic Plan*, p. 10.

[114] Ibid.

[115] For example, the gains in winter, summer, and annual water clarity in 2012 may be due to stormwater management efforts or to decreased precipitation last year, which led to decreased total levels of runoff, or some combination of both. *TERC State of the Lake Report 2013*.

[116] For example, see Anne Knowles, "With 38 pipes Draining into Lake Tahoe Are Lake Clarity Efforts Worth a Billion Bucks?" *Lake Tahoe News*, January 17, 2012.

[117] Examples include Tahoe Regional Planning Agency and the Tahoe Environmental Research Center. See *TRPA Strategic Plan*, p. 9.

[118] *TRPA Strategic Plan*, p. 9.

[119] For example, see public comments recorded in Tahoe Regional Planning Agency, *Advisory Planning Commision Meeting*, August 3, 2011, http://www.trpa.org/wp-content/uploads/aug_2011_apc_packet.pdf.

[120] Richard Frank, "Environmentalists Sue Over New Lake Tahoe Plan: Is the Perfect the Enemy of the Good," *Legal Planet*, February 20, 2013.

[121] *State of the Lake Report 2013*.

[122] *TRPA EIP Update*.

[123] *TRPA Strategic Plan*, p. 5.

[124] Adam Jensen, "TRPA Approves Lake Tahoe Regional Plan Update, 12-1," *Tahoe Daily Tribune*, December 12, 2021. http://www.tahoedailytribune.com/article/20121212/NEWS/121219952.

[125] *TRPA Strategic Plan*, p. 8.

[126] For example, see *Sierra Club and Friends of the West Shore v. Tahoe Regional Planning Agency* (California Eastern District Court 2013).

[127] Darcie Goodman-Collins, "Excited to Move Forward with Nevada on Board," *Tahoe Daily Tribune*, June 13, 2013 (Guest Column by the League to Save Lake Tahoe Executive Director).

[128] Office of Governor Edmund G. Brown Jr., press release, May 14, 2013, http://gov.ca.gov/news.php?id=18041.

[129] Shelly Aldean and Casey Beyer, *Moving Forward for Lake Tahoe*, Tahoe Regional Planning Agency, April 2013, http://www.trpa.org/wp-content/uploads/COLUMN_GB_Compact_April_2013.pdf.

[130] These changes have already been signed into Nevada state law. California state bill SB 630 would amend the Compact to match changes made by Nevada if approved by the California legislature. SB 630 was approved by the State Assembly on September 9, 2013, and by the state Senate on September 10, 2013; it is now awaiting the governor's signature.

[131] *Sierra Club and Friends of the West Shore v. Tahoe Regional Planning Agency* (California Eastern District Court 2013).

[132] Observations recorded by Tahoe Environmental Research Center at UC Davis. Found in *TERC State of the Lake 2013*.

[133] *TERC State of the Lake Report 2013*, Executive Summary.

[134] For example, 2011 was one of the wettest and coldest winters on record.

[135] Robert Coats and Kelly Redmond, *Climate Change in the Tahoe Basin*, Tahoe Science Consortium, 2011, http://www.tahoescience.org/wp-content/uploads/2011/10/LTFedEvent-2008-Climate-Change-WQ-Poster.pdf.

[136] US Army Corps of Engineers, *Lake Tahoe Region Aquatic Invasive Species Management Plan, California-Nevada*, September 2009, http://anstaskforce.gov/State Plans/Lake_Tahoe_Region_AIS_Management_Plan.pdf

[137] Since 1969, the stratification season has been extended by an average of 25 days. *TERC State of the Lake Report 2013*.

[138] *TERC State of the Lake 2013*, Section 8.10.

[139] Anoxia refers to the total depletion of oxygen in the water, in this case the bottom waters of Lake Tahoe. Due to the lack of mixing in the bottom waters, TERC is currently monitoring oxygen levels in the deepest part of the lake to determine the rate at which oxygen is being lost when mixing does not occur. *TERC State of the Lake 2013*, Section 2; Lisa Borre, "Warming Lakes: Effects of Climate Change Seen on Lake Tahoe," *National Geographic Water Currents*, October 17, 2012, at http://newswatch.nationalgeographic.com/2012/10/17/warming-lakes-effects-of-climate-change-seen-on-lake-tahoe/.

[140] Forest Management Plans are comprehensive plans, created with input from the public and scientific communities. They detail the objectives the USFS has for a specific national forest (in this case Tahoe National Forest) and include management plans (i.e., timber management, hazardous fuel management, and climate change adaptation) to achieve the objectives.

[141] See Section 8 and Section 12 of S. 1451.

[142] See Section 12 of S. 1451.

[143] *TRPA Threshold Evaluation*.

[144] *Trees in Transition*.

In: Ecosystem Restoration   ISBN: 978-1-63117-540-4
Editor: Simon Acheson   © 2014 Nova Science Publishers, Inc.

Chapter 2

OVERVIEW OF MANAGEMENT AND RESTORATION ACTIVITIES IN THE SALTON SEA[*]

Pervaze A. Sheikh and Charles V. Stern

SUMMARY

The Salton Sea is located in southern California and is considered the largest inland water body in the state. The Salton Basin, where the Salton Sea is located, has supported many lakes and water bodies throughout its geological history. The Salton Sea was created when a canal gate broke in 1905 allowing fresh Colorado River water into the Basin. The Salton Sea is now sustained by agricultural runoff from farmlands in the Imperial and Coachella valleys. It provides permanent and temporary habitat for many species of plants and animals, including several endangered species. It also serves as an important recreational area for the region. The Salton Sea has been altered by increasing salinity and decreasing size caused by steadily decreasing water flows into the Sea. High salinity levels and shrinking area have been linked to habitat changes and stressed populations of plants and animals, economic losses in the region, and impaired air quality.

---

[*] This is an edited, reformatted and augmented version of a Congressional Research Service publication, CRS Report for Congress R43211, dated September 24, 2013.

Efforts to restore the Salton Sea ecosystem have been discussed and initiated through state and federal actions. Several studies by state and federal agencies have provided baseline data about the Sea, and some restoration plans have been proposed. The State of California, the Salton Sea Authority, and the federal government through the Bureau of Reclamation have devised plans for restoring the Sea. However, none of these plans are being fully implemented. Federal authorities that address restoration of the Salton Sea are generally based on creating and evaluating proposals for restoration, rather than implementing restoration activities in a comprehensive manner similar to other initiatives in the Everglades and Great Lakes. California is pursuing restoration options, but funding for implementing them is lacking.

Whether or not to restore the Salton Sea remains controversial. Proponents of restoration contend that the Salton Sea ecosystem is valuable from an ecological standpoint because it is one of the few remaining large-scale wetland habitats in California for migratory birds and fish. Further, some argue that keeping the Salton Sea intact will stimulate economic development, recreation, and tourism in the region. They note that losing the Sea could cause economic and environmental decline, and could lead to air quality problems from exposed seabeds. Others contend that the Sea should not be restored. They argue that the Salton Sea is naturally declining, as it has throughout its geological history. Further, they note that countering this process will be costly and ultimately not worth the expense. They state that limited restoration funds should be used to restore other natural wetlands in California, such as the Sacramento-San Joaquin Bay Delta.

The decline of the Salton Sea ecosystem is accelerating due to water transfers from agricultural lands to municipal water districts in San Diego under the terms of the Quantification Settlement Agreement, an agreement on how to share California's apportionment of Colorado River water. The water transfers have resulted in less water flowing into the Salton Sea and accelerated increases in salinity and shoreline recession. According to some scientists, salinity levels may reach lethal levels for most fish and wildlife as soon as 2018. These predictions, along with the steadily declining ecosystem might provoke Congress to consider a larger role in restoration for the federal government. Congress may decide to address restoration by increasing the federal role in restoration efforts. This could be done by funding existing federal authorities that address, or could address, restoring the ecosystem; authorizing federal participation and appropriations for implementing existing restoration plans; or authorizing a new comprehensive plan to be created that might involve participation from federal and non-federal stakeholders, similar to other restoration initiatives around the country. Congress might also decide not to address restoration of the Salton Sea ecosystem, or simply maintain the status quo of federal participation.

INTRODUCTION

The Salton Sea is located in southern California and is considered the largest inland water body in the state. The Salton Sea was formed in 1905 when the Colorado River broke through a canal gate, allowing water to flow into the Salton Basin uninterrupted for 18 months. Since its formation, the Sea has been maintained largely through agricultural runoff from surrounding areas. The Salton Sea was not the first body of water in the basin; several other lakes have existed in the Basin throughout its geological history. The creation of the Salton Sea in 1905 eventually led to development of its shoreline and its waters were stocked with sportfish. Until the late 1960s, the Salton Sea was one of the most prolific sport fisheries in the country, with a high diversity of birds and wildlife. The Salton Sea also serves as an important wetland area along the Pacific Flyway, a migratory route for birds stretching from Alaska to Patagonia.

The ecology and economy surrounding the Salton Sea has deteriorated steadily over the past several decades due, in part, to a changing ecosystem marked by decreasing water flows and increasing salinity. The Salton Sea has shrunk due to evaporation and declining water inflows, resulting in increased salinity and deteriorating fish and wildlife habitat. High salinity levels combined with toxic concentrations of substances have led to disease and widespread mortality of fish and birds.[1] Current saline levels are nearing fatal levels for all fish, leading some scientists to predict that fatal saline levels will occur by 2018.[2] The subsequent population decline of fish could have severe effects on migratory birds that use the Salton Sea as a primary stopover point on the Pacific Flyway. Furthermore, exposed lake beds could allow toxins and dust to enter the air, which could lead to air pollution and human health problems.

Attention to the ecological condition of the Salton Sea and efforts to restore the Sea have existed for several decades. However, interest in the ecological health of the Salton Sea has amplified since 2003, when the Quantification Settlement Agreement (QSA) was signed by several water districts in California, the state of California, and the Department of the Interior (DOI), and signed into California law. QSA requires California to gradually reduce its consumption of Colorado River water to 4.4 million acre-feet a year (AFY) through voluntary agriculture-to-urban water transfers and other water efficiency measures.[3] The implementation of this agreement has resulted in less water flowing into the Salton Sea, thus accelerating its ecological decline. However, as part of the QSA, participating water districts agreed to contribute $163 million toward mitigation and restoration. In addition, the water districts agreed to provide 200,000 AFY of Colorado River water to the Sea though December 31, 2017. While some of these mitigation efforts have been implemented, longer-term restoration efforts and the distribution of these costs are still contested and uncertain.

Congressional concern for restoring the Salton Sea stems, in part, from the value of the Sea as habitat for federal and state listed endangered species, as well as other migrating and resident bird species; a reservoir for agricultural drainage waters; a center for recreation; and a large wetland ecosystem, among other things.[4] Concerns over air pollution from exposed sea beds have also been expressed by Members of Congress.[5] These concerns have been reflected, in part, by efforts to address the restoration of the Salton Sea and its ecosystem. Congress has passed laws addressing the restoration of the Salton Sea and authorized funds for restoring the Salton Sea in the Water Resources Development Act of 2007.[6] Current restoration efforts have been led mainly by the state and local governments.

Consensus around restoring the Salton Sea has not been fully attained. Some contend that the Salton Sea should not be restored.[7] They argue that the geological history of the Salton Sea demonstrates a pattern of water bodies naturally shrinking and disappearing, and then reforming over time. They note that the Salton Sea will follow a similar process and that countering this natural process will be costly and ultimately not worth the cost. These opponents argue that the restoration funds should instead be used to restore other natural wetlands in California, such as the Sacramento and San Joaquin rivers' delta confluence with San Francisco Bay (Bay-Delta). To counter this argument, some respond by noting that the natural inflows of water into the Salton Sea have been artificially diverted by humans when the Colorado River was diverted into a canal and that natural processes and cycles will not exist again with these structures in place. Further, they note that the value of restoring the Salton Sea lies in its ecological significance as a large wetland along the Pacific Flyway and a habitat for fish and wildlife, and its potential to stimulate economic development in the region through tourism, recreation, and energy development.

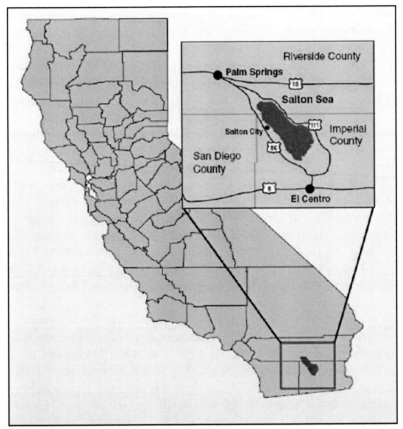

Source: California Legislative Analyst's Office. Restoring the Salton Sea. January 24, 2008, http://www.lao.ca.gov/2008/rsrc/salton_sea/salton_sea_01-24-08.aspx.

Figure 1. Map of Salton Sea and Vicinity.

BACKGROUND

Geological and Ecological Characteristics of the Salton Sea

The Salton Sea is located in southern California and is considered the largest inland water body in the state. The Salton Basin, where the Salton Sea is located, has supported many lakes and water bodies throughout its geological history. The last of these prehistoric water bodies was Lake

Cahuilla, which dried up nearly 400 years ago. In 1901, a portion of the Colorado River was diverted through the Imperial canal to irrigate agricultural fields in the Salton Basin. Waterflowed through the New Alamo River and into the Imperial Valley from this channel.[8] In 1905, water from spring floods broke through a canal head-gate diverting a portion of the Colorado River into the Basin and forming the Salton Sea. Water flowed uninterrupted for nearly 18 months into the Salton Sea before it could be redirected to the Gulf of California. The new Sea formed as a closed basin with no outlets, which is still its condition today. The Sea consisted largely of fresh water at its inception; however, the water immediately began to evaporate and increase in salinity.

The construction of Hoover Dam and the All American Canal in 1928 allowed water from the Colorado River to be transferred directly to the Imperial Valley for irrigation. After flowing through agricultural lands, this water drained into the Salton Sea, thereby preventing the Sea from evaporating. In 1924 and 1928, President Coolidge executed Public Water Reserve Orders 90 and 114 for the withdrawal of lands located in and around the Salton Sea.[9] These lands were designated as a repository for agricultural, subsurface, and surface water drainage.

The ecosystem properties of the Salton Sea are largely determined by its water level, chemical and salt concentration, and balance between the rate of evaporation and water inflow. Nearly 75% of the water flowing into the Sea comes from agricultural runoff originating in the Imperial and Coachella valleys in California, the other 25% is from rain and other surface inflows.[10] As water in the Sea evaporates, the concentration of salt increases. Presently, the salinity level in the Sea is approximately 52 parts per thousand (ppt), which is approximately 50% greater than ocean water and one-fifth that of the Great Salt Lake in Utah (270 ppt) (See **Figure 2**).[11] At 52 ppt, the Salton Sea is considered to be hypersaline. High salinity combines with extreme eutrophication to cause fish kills in the Sea. Eutrophication can result in anoxic conditions leading to fish death.[12]

In 1950, the Sea reached salinity levels similar to the Pacific Ocean. At this time, the California Department of Fish and Game began transferring saltwater fish species to the Sea. During the 1950s, and in the next two decades, the Sea became a popular destination for sport fishing and tourism. However, changes to the Sea, including flooding of resort areas and wildlife habitat, bird and fish die-offs, and health threats of untreated water, led to a decline in recreation and development around the Sea in the 1960s.[13] The current salinity levels in the Sea are too high to support the former diversity of fish. The most ubiquitous species in the Salton Sea now is the tilapia

(*Oreochromis mossambicus*), which was introduced by farmers to control weeds in their ponds in 1964.[14] In addition, the Sea also houses the endangered desert pupfish (*Cyprinodon macularius*), the only native fish species in the Sea. Deteriorating water quality has also had a large detrimental impact on the invertebrate life in the Sea, such as on pileworms and barnacles, two important components of the Salton Sea food web.[15] Currently, few fish can survive in the hypersaline waters of the Sea. Future salinity predictions indicate that all species of fish may disappear from the Sea as early as 2023.[16]

The Salton Sea ecosystem provides a variety of habitat for fish and wildlife species, including open water, estuaries, salt marshes, and riparian corridors. Due to the loss of wetland habitat in southern California and throughout the state's vast Central Valley, the Salton Sea is a primary stopover point for birds on the Pacific Flyway.[17] The Sea supports more than 400 species of resident and migratory birds, of which more than 50 are species of special status (including three listed under the Endangered Species Act[18] (ESA)).[19] Surveys have estimated that the total population of birds in the Salton Sea can reach up to 500,000 birds per month.[20] Many of these birds are piscivorous, relying on fish in the Salton Sea for sustenance. Other birds can feed on both the fish and invertebrates found in the basin.

The mortality of bird and fish species in and around the Salton Sea is of concern because of federal and state listed endangered species that inhabit the Sea. For example, the Yuma clapper rail (*Rallus longirostris yumanensis*) is a federally listed endangered species, residing in and around the Sea during the year. Other state listed species of special interest, such as the peregrine falcon (*Falco peregrinus*) and the bald eagle (*Haliaeetus leucocephalus*), are occasionally seen at the Sea as they make their way along the Pacific Flyway. The desert pupfish (*Cyprinodon macularius*) is the only endemic fish species in the Salton Basin, and was listed as a federally endangered species in 1986.

Conserving endangered species in the Salton Basin is one of the objectives of the Salton Sea Authority, which was chartered by the State of California in 1993 to remedy problems facing the Salton Sea. The Salton Sea Authority is a "joint powers" agency chartered to ensure the beneficial uses of the Salton Sea, such as maintaining the Sea as an agricultural drainage reservoir, restoring the wildlife resources and habitats around and in the Sea, stimulating recreational use, and providing an environment for economic development around the Sea. This agency is comprised of representatives from Riverside and Imperial counties, the Coachella Valley Water District, the Imperial Irrigation District, and the Torres Martinez Desert Cahuilla Tribe. Federal and state agencies have representatives on the Authority as *ex-officio* members.[21]

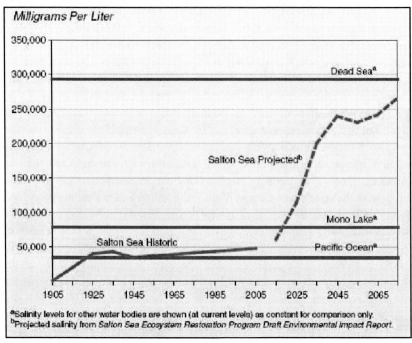

Source: California Legislative Analyst's Office. Restoring the Salton Sea. January 24, 2008, http://www.lao.ca.gov.

Figure 2.Trend in Salinity Levels.

Salton Sea and the Quantification Settlement Agreement

Farmlands in the Imperial and Coachella valleys have historically been irrigated with approximately 3.3 million AFY of Colorado River water.[22] From this amount, the Salton Sea received approximately 1.4 million AFY of this water in the form of agricultural runoff. However, under the Quantification Settlement Agreement (QSA), which was passed in October 2003, around 300,000 AFY of Colorado River water that flows from these valleys are being supplied to other urban water districts and not all reaching the Salton Sea.[23] (See below for a summary of the QSA.) These agriculture-to-urban transfers will reduce agricultural inflows to the Sea by an estimated 30% by 2018, according to stakeholders. The Bureau of Reclamation modeled flow changes after 2018 with the implementation of the QSA and determined that 95% of all future inflows would less than or equal to 835,000 AFY between 2018 and

2077, with a mean of all inflows equaling 727,000 AFY.[24] The Salton Sea Authority estimated a relatively similar scenario, where water flowing to the Salton Sea would stabilize at 800,000 AFY after 2018 with the implementation of the QSA (see **Figure 3**).[25]

QUANTIFICATION SETTLEMENT AGREEMENT (QSA)

Seven western U.S. states (Colorado, Utah, Wyoming, New Mexico, Arizona, California, and Nevada) signed the Colorado River Compact in 1922, agreeing to specified allotments of Colorado River water. California was apportioned 4.4 million acre-feet a year (AFY) of Colorado River water. However, California had historically used an additional 800,000 AFY over this allocation.[26] This occurred because other states in the Compact were withdrawing less than their allocation. As other states increased their water consumption, the water available for California has been reduced. In 1996, the Secretary of the Interior required California to develop and enact a strategy to reduce its water consumption to 4.4 million AFY before the secretary would approve any further cooperative water transfers between California agencies. This strategy became known as the Colorado River Water Use Plan (California Plan).

The QSA was designed to help implement components of the California Plan by serving as a contractual agreement between the Imperial Irrigation District (IID), the Coachella Valley Water District (CVWD), the San Diego County Water Authority (SDCWA), the Municipal Water District of Southern California (MWD), the state, and the U.S. Department of the Interior (DOI).[27] The agreement established long-term (45-75 years) transfers of agricultural water from IID to SDCWA and MWD for urban use.[28] Around 300,000 AFY would be transferred; the water to be transferred would come from fallowing of or other water efficiency measures on agricultural lands. Starting in 2021, 200,000 AFY will be transferred to SDCWA; up to an additional 110,000 AFY will be transferred to MWD.[29] Over this long-term agreement, over 18.3 million acre-feet of water will be diverted from agriculture to urban use in San Diego.[30] State legislation implementing the QSA also has multiple mitigation measures that are to be implemented to restore the Salton Sea. They range from medium-term water transfers to funding restoration actions.

Further, legislation requires that the state identify a Salton Sea restoration plan and a funding plan to implement it. In 2007, the state identified and submitted a restoration plan to the state legislature with an estimated cost of $8.9 billion. The plan has not been implemented and a funding plan has not been approved.

The QSA was passed and authorized under California law in October of 2003. Since 2003, there have been multiple, ongoing challenges to the validity of the agreement. On July 31, 2013, the Sacramento Superior Court issued the final ruling on all 12 separate agreements within the QSA. The court concluded that IID's actions in entering and executing the 12 QSA agreements were valid and upheld the legality of the water transfers.

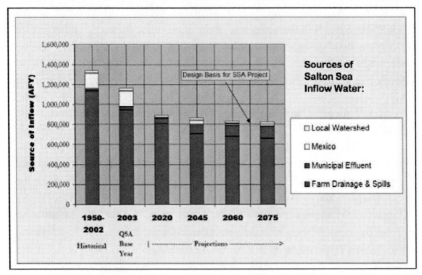

Source: Salton Sea Authority, *Salton Sea Authority Plan for Multi-Purpose Project*, La Quinta, CA, June 29, 2006, p. 11.

Figure 3. Predicted Water Flows into the Salton Sea.

The QSA contains multiple provisions to mitigate environmental effects of its implementation on the Salton Sea, including the following:

- IID is to directly transport 200,000 AFY of Colorado River water to the Salton Sea for 15 years from 2003 to January 1, 2018.[31]

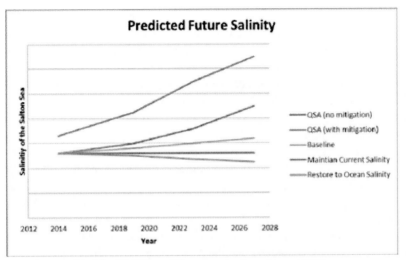

Source: Pervaze Sheikh. CRS Natural Resource Analyst. August 2013.

Note: QSA with mitigation and the baseline separate around 2018 due to salinity reaching 60 ppt (when water transfers end). After the Sea passes 60 ppt, mitigation does not include salinity control measures to keep the Sea's salinity consistent with the baseline; it only includes species habitat construction and management in the area.

Figure 4. Salton Sea Salinity Under Different Restoration Paths.

- IID, CVWD, and SDCWA are to provide $133 million for environmental mitigation related to the water transfers, and for IID to deposit an additional $30 million into a restoration fund.[32]
- The State of California is to assume all additional costs of mitigation and restoration. The legality of this cost provision was recently upheld.
- Concurrent legislation also set up a Salton Sea Restoration Fund (SSRF), overseen by the Department of Fish and Game to be used for environmental and engineering projects (Fish and Game Code Section 2931).[33]
- The California Secretary for Resources, in consultation with the Salton Sea Authority, was to present the state legislature with a preferred alternative restoration plan for the Salton Sea by December 31, 2006.[34]

In addition, this legislation stated that restoration of the Salton Sea was of state and national interest; it authorized the state to develop a long-term, adaptive conservation and restoration plan for species in the Salton Sea. However, the development and implementation of any restoration plan is conditional on the state legislature appropriating funds and not required by the QSA.[35] The California Secretary for Resources was required to present the state legislature with a preferred alternative restoration plan, but there is no requirement to implement or fund this preferred alternative.[36] Some have used this premise to assert that there is no unconditional obligation for the State of California to develop and implement a long-term restoration plan that would aim to restore the Sea to a previous state that could support the fish and migratory birds that currently reside and visit there (for a visual representation of mitigation versus restoration impacts in salinity, see **Figure 4**).

There is still disagreement on the extent to which the state is responsible for restoration. Some contend that the recent state court ruling established that the QSA requires the state to restore the Salton Sea.[37] However, in recent QSA litigation, IID and CVWD have argued that actual Salton Sea restoration was never a commitment by the state. The state legislation implementing the QSA requires IID, CVWD, SDCWA, and the State of California to fund the costs of environmental mitigation deemed necessary to avoid environmental harm due to the water transfers.[38] The Environmental Impact Assessment determined that appropriate mitigation could be met by 200,000 AFY of Colorado River water transferred annually to the Salton Sea for the first 15 years after water transfers commenced; the construction of a pupfish refugium pond and the development of a plan to provide pupfish connectivity between drains; up to 652 acres, and at least 190 acres, of managed marsh for rail birds; two roost sites for brown pelicans; monitoring programs for all state and federally listed species; and a study program to determine the impacts of selenium on wildlife.[39] IID, CVWD, and SDCWA, were required to pay up to $133 million of these environmental mitigation costs, with the state required to pay any and all additional costs, regardless of legislative appropriations.[40] IID, CVWD, and SDCWA also agreed to place $30 million into the Salton Sea Restoration Fund (SSRF).[41]

Environmental Concerns in the Salton Sea

Some contend that the most pressing issue for the Salton Sea is increasingly high salinity. Some experts state that, without intervention, the

Salton Sea will reach fatal salinity levels for most aquatic wildlife in the Sea between 2018 and 2028. Scientists have predicted that the Salton Sea could exceed 60 ppt by 2018 after the water transfers under the Quantitative Settlement Agreement (QSA) ramp up and mitigation water transfers to the Sea end.[42] According to some, salinity levels beyond 40 ppt might result in fish with limited reproductive success, suppressed immune systems, and physiological stress.[43] At 60 ppt and above, the water would be too saline to support tilapia, the main food source for birds in the area. Some contend that the Salton Sea would have naturally increased in salinity over time, thereby reducing its ability to sustain aquatic wildlife.[44] Others describe increasing salinity in the Sea as predominately a result of human activities (e.g. water transfers and agriculture), which have decreased the potential for restoration.[45]

Other water quality issues, such as toxic chemicals and low oxygen levels, are also directly related, in part, to diminishing water flows. Toxic levels of selenium and elevated levels of Dichlorodiphenyldichloroethylene (DDE) have been found in the Sea. These substances have been detected at toxic levels in fish and wildlife in and around the Sea. Both DDE and selenium can cause reproductive problems in fish and birds.[46] In addition, DDE and selenium can have adverse health effects on humans.[47] Some contend that toxic levels of these substances were attained due to agricultural areas being the main source of water inflows to the Sea.[48] There were widely publicized mortalities of fish and birds in and around the Salton Sea in the 1990s thought to be associated with toxins.[49] In 1996, an estimated 15% to 20% of the western population of white pelicans and more than 1,000 endangered brown pelicans died.[50] In August 1999, more than 7.6 million tilapia and croakers died due to low levels of dissolved oxygen in the Sea.[51]

Water quality issues have raised concerns about the future of endangered species that depend on the Salton Sea ecosystem. The loss of fish populations in the Sea could significantly reduce and possibly eliminate use of the Salton Sea by piscivorous birds by the early 2020s, according to some scientists.[52] Some state and federally listed piscivorous birds such as the Yuma clapper rail (federal and state endangered) could be affected initially. Some invertebrates and possibly desert pupfish could survive at higher salinity levels, according to some scientists. For example, desert pupfish have survived in waters with salinity as high as 90 ppt in various locations.[53] Some birds that rely on both fish and invertebrates may still be able to forage under high salinity conditions; however, the species composition of birds would be expected to change as the makeup of invertebrates shifts due to changes in salinity. Some nonnative fish species might still be found in the Salton Basin in areas of lower salinity around the Salton Sea, such as the rivers, creeks, and agricultural drains that feed into the Sea.[54]

Air pollution may emerge as an environmental issue as the Salton Sea shrinks in size. As the shoreline recedes, areas of lake bed would be exposed to heat and wind. As the lake bed dries and erodes, dust could enter the air and be circulated across large areas. Air-borne dust from dry beds in the Sea could contain harmful levels of pesticides, herbicides, and naturally occurring selenium.[55] People in the surrounding Coachella and Imperial counties could be affected by this contaminated dust and contract respiratory problems. Presently, some counties near the Salton Sea have significantly higher rates of respiratory problems compared to other nearby counties.[56] While there are many possible causes for these increased numbers of respiratory issues around the Salton Sea area, some attribute the problems, in part, to contaminated air derived from dry areas around the Salton Sea.[57] Some also note that salt in the dust upwelling from dry areas around the Sea can damage crops. The Pacific Institute has estimated that the loss of water due to water transfers will expose an additional 130 square miles of seabed and increase the amount of dust in the air by a third over what is currently found.[58] The Salton Sea Authority estimates that if the Sea dries up, the cost to mitigate the effects of dust alone will be upwards of $1 billion, with annual maintenance cost of around $48 million.[59]

In the fall of 2012, a strong southern wind stirred the Salton Sea waters, bringing decayed material to the surface. This released hydrogen sulfide and produced a very strong rancid odor that was reported more than 200 miles away in both Simi Valley and Los Angeles County.[60] This incident was dubbed the "Big Stink" and captured the attention of national media outlets. After this incident, funds were allocated to install monitoring equipment to measure gases rising from the sea.[61] While there are no known human health concerns linked to the odorous gases, the incident stimulated attention about the poor condition of the Salton Sea, according to some.[62] Further, the hydrogen sulfide released from the Sea (the source of the smell) consumes oxygen in Sea waters. This could result in fish kills, and if severe enough, could deplete all the oxygen in the Sea and cause the ecosystem to collapse.

Restoration Efforts in the Salton Sea

Some of the ecological problems in the Salton Sea were foreseen by scientists who noted that salinity in the Sea was increasing at a rate that would eventually render the Sea uninhabitable for fish and wildlife. Early studies focused on understanding the hydrological and saline properties of the Sea. Since then, several federal, state, and private entities have developed proposals to restore the Sea, primarily by controlling its salinity and maintaining its water level.

Federal efforts to restore the Salton Sea can be traced to the passage of the Reclamation Projects Authorization and Adjustment Act of 1992 (Title XI, §1101 of P.L. 102-575).[63] The act directed the Secretary of the Interior to conduct research on projects to control salinity levels, provide habitat for endangered species, enhance fisheries, and protect recreational values in the Salton Sea. Seven years later, authorized restoration activities in the Salton Sea expanded with the passage of the Salton Sea Recovery Act of 1998 (P.L. 105-372). This act authorized the Secretary of the Interior to conduct feasibility studies and economic analyses of various options for restoring the Salton Sea. Further, the secretary was authorized to conduct studies of wildlife and species' responses to the hydrology and toxicology of the Sea.[64] This act also authorized river reclamation activities for the New and Alamo Rivers (tributaries that flow into the Salton Sea). In addition, several restoration projects have been administered through the state-funded Salton Sea Authority, including efforts in collaboration with the U.S. Bureau of Reclamation (BOR).

Early restoration work conducted by both state and federal entities consisted of feasibility studies focused on solar pools and salt evaporation technology.[65] Both of these approaches aim to reduce the salinity of the Salton Sea by evaporating a portion of the seawater and disposing resulting salt deposits. To maintain a steady sea level, water from the Colorado River would need to flow into and mix with the Salton Sea. In 2004, the Salton Sea Authority released a restoration plan for the Salton Sea that called for the construction of a causeway across the center of the Sea.[66] This was eventually incorporated into the 2006 *Salton Sea Authority Plan for Multi-Purpose Project*.[67] The plan proposed to split the Salton Sea into two pools. However, when the QSA was first upheld by court in 2007, some suggested that the acquisition of water from the Colorado River necessary for salinity control technologies would be physically and politically infeasible.[68] In its study analyzing options for restoring the Salton Sea, the Secretary of the Interior was not authorized to consider any option that relies on importing new or additional water from the Colorado River.[69]

CURRENT RESTORATION IN THE SALTON SEA

State Actions in the Salton Basin

Restoration activities and studies regarding the Salton Sea have been mainly funded and managed by the State of California. The state has increasingly endorsed the use of Saline Habitat Complexes (SHCs) to maintain viable ecosystems for current wildlife. These complexes would be constructed with berms or other barriers to create shallow saline pools. The salinity in these pools could vary and would be maintained by 'blended water', or possibly geothermal-powered desalinated Salton seawater. State efforts to restore the Salton Sea are, in part, due to provisions in the QSA which require the California Secretary for Resources, in consultation with the SSA, to present the state legislature with a preferred alternative for restoration. This state-identified preferred alternative was published as the Salton Sea Ecosystem Restoration Final Programmatic Environmental Impact Report (PEIR) and presented to the legislature in May of 2007.[70]

The state-identified preferred alternative included SHCs in the northern and southern end of the Sea, a marine sea formed by barriers, air quality management facilities, a brine sink for discharge of salts, conveyance facilities, and sedimentation distribution facilities. In addition, the preferred alternative included Early Start Habitat, areas for geothermal development, and connectivity waterways for desert pupfish (See **Figure 5** for the plan).[71] The final cost for the state preferred alternative is estimated at $8.9 billion (in 2006 dollars).[72] After construction is completed, the expected annual operations and maintenance costs are $142 million (in 2006 dollars). No state action has been taken to authorize funding for this plan. However, the state is proceeding to implement pilot studies that measure the effectiveness of SHCs, with federal assistance. For example, the state has a Salton Sea Species Conservation Habitat Project plan that is nearing completion.[73] The aim of this project is to create up to 3,770 acres of SHCs for conserving and protecting fish and wildlife species that depend upon the Salton Sea. Pools would be created at the southern end of the Salton Sea on land owned by Imperial Irrigation District or the federal government. The project is not intended to be a comprehensive restoration project for the Salton Sea, but rather a "proof of concept" project to see if SHCs along the edge of the Sea can sustain fish and wildlife. The project would affect jurisdictional waters, and thus, requires the U.S. Army Corps of Engineers (Corps) to assess the project and provide necessary permits for construction. The Corps, in conjunction with the state, released a Final Environmental Impact Statement/Environmental Impact Recommendation in July 2013.[74] The Corps is expected to use the EIS/EIR in determining whether to issue a Department of the Army permit for this project under section 404 of the Clean Water Act.

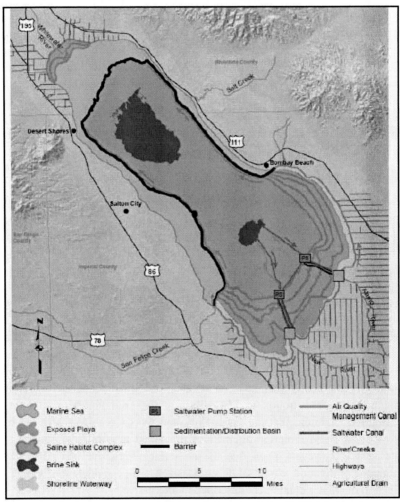

Source: California Department of Fish and Game and the California Department of Water Resources, *Salton Sea Ecosystem Restoration Program: Preferred Alternative and Funding Plan*, May 2007. p. 8.

Figure 5. State Preferred Plan.

In addition to the state-identified plan, the SSA continues to seek funding and support at both the state and federal level for its 2006 plan involving the separation of the Sea into two lakes (see "Restoration Efforts in the Salton Sea" for more details on the SSA Plan). In recent negotiations between IID and County of Imperial, both parties have endorsed the SSA 2006 Plan.[75]

The state legislature is addressing Salton Sea issues through legislation. For example, state bill AB71 would require the California Natural Resources Agency, in consultation and coordination with the Salton Sea Authority, to lead Salton Sea restoration efforts.[76] Efforts would include several investigations into restoration projects. Further, the bill would authorize the Salton Sea Authority to lead a restoration and funding study to address restoring the Salton Sea and provide input to the Secretary of the California Natural Resources Agency on various aspects of restoration and air quality in the region.

Federal Actions in the Salton Basin

Federal actions directed towards restoring the Salton Sea are not following any comprehensive plan. Restoration efforts by federal agencies are largely in the form of pilot projects, monitoring, and individual agency plans or proposals. For example, BOR created and disseminated a study assessing restoration possibilities in 2007.[77] The development of the study was authorized and required under P.L. 108-361. Section 201 states that the Secretary of the Interior, in coordination with the State of California and the Salton Sea Authority (SSA), shall complete a feasibility study on a preferred alternative for restoration. The BOR study provided five alternative restoration plans and a no action alternative, with costs for implementing the alternatives ranging from $3.5 billion to $14 billion.[78] BOR did not state a preferred alternative, claiming that the uncertainty and risks, combined with the high costs of all five restoration alternatives prevented it from recommending an alternative. However, given that the no-action alternative had $1.4 billion estimated mitigation costs, BOR emphasized that consideration should be given to the SHCs component described in alternative 5.

BOR and USGS created a pilot study consisting of a small series of SHCs from 2006 to 2010 to determine whether these complexes could be a feasible restoration approach.[79] The pilot study concluded that SHCs, and similar saline complexes, could minimize the risks and costs of restoration, while restoring wildlife habitat and partially mitigating air quality impacts. However, selenium concentrations in these pools were reported at potentially toxic levels, which would warrant observation and study to see how it might adversely affect fish and wildlife. Overall, the study was reported to demonstrate that the SHP model is a viable alternative for restoring wetlands at the Salton Sea, but that the potential risks of selenium need to be considered.[80]

As noted above, the Corps is also involved in pilot studies concerning SHCs. The Water Resources Development Act of 2007 (P.L. 110-114) authorized the Secretary of the Army to review the state-approved plan, the "Salton Sea Ecosystem Restoration Program Preferred Alternative Report and Funding Plan", and implement feasible pilot projects described in the plan.[81] Under WRDA 2007, if the secretary determines the projects are feasible, then he is authorized to enter into an agreement with the state to help implement the pilot projects.[82] One of these pilot projects is the previously mentioned Salton Sea Species Conservation Habitat Project plan. The Administration has requested $200,000 of federal funding for a reconnaissance study of the plan. The request is in the Corps FY2014 budget request.[83]

Additional Restoration Measures

In addition to proposed comprehensive plans to restore the Salton Sea, several have endorsed site- specific plans or activities for restoration. For example, local and state efforts have been made to fund and explore the development of renewable and biofuel energy sources in the Salton Sea.[84] The Sea has multiple potential renewable energy sources that include geothermal energy, solar power, and bio-algae. It has been estimated that the Salton Sea Basin could support up to 2,000 megawatts (MW) of economically feasible renewable energy capacity.[85] A large portion of this capacity- around 1,400 MW- would be geothermal. The rest would be solar, which some proposed could be constructed along acres of the exposed lake beds around the Sea.

Currently, IID generates approximately 600 MW of geothermal energy in the Basin.[86] IID has been developing a pilot study to use geothermal energy to desalinate water to create saline habitat pools. The Torres-Martinez Tribe has also requested funding from the State of California to construct a solar photovoltaic field to power reliable and sustainable water delivery to the saline habitat ponds on its land.[87] If these pilot studies indicate that the use of renewable energy for desalination is feasible, it could allow for previously discussed salinity control methods to be used. The desalinated water could be a substitute for the fresh Colorado River water that would otherwise be necessary for salt evaporation and salinity control in the Basin.

In addition, SSA has been discussing a partnership with the Salton Sea Action Committee (SSAC), which represents some of the private business in the area interested in energy development. The SSAC is interested in promoting the development of renewable energy (e.g., solar fields and geothermal) in the Basin to generate funds for restoration. Further, there is discussion about creating an Infrastructure Finance District in the area, which would use a portion of proceeds from development to fund restoration. The SSAC contends that this arrangement would allow local governments to take on infrastructure and other projects (e.g., geothermal and other energy plants) and generate funds necessary for maintaining the Sea for fish and migratory birds.[88]

Some others have proposed the production bio-algae as a mechanism to both provide funds for restoration and improve the environmental health of the Salton Sea. Researchers at Clemson University have developed a Controlled Eutrophication Process (CEP) to grow algae in the Sea.[89] Preliminary studies have shown that CEP would improve water quality, increase fish production, and have a potential sizable revenue stream.[90]

POTENTIAL ISSUES FOR CONGRESS

Progress towards restoring the Salton Sea has been slow in recent years, largely due to the lack of a comprehensive plan to guide efforts and lack of funding. Indeed, some contend that there is not full consensus behind restoring the Sea. Those against restoration contend that it will naturally shrink and disappear, making attempts at restoration futile and expensive in the long term.[91] Others counter these claims by stating the Sea is in an artificial state of decline because of its reliance on agricultural runoff artificially conveyed from the Colorado River. Further, they add that the increasing salinity of the Sea along with its shrinkage will cause irreparable damage to the ecosystem and negatively affect fish and wildlife populations, as well as create health risks for humans due to contaminated dusts.

Some contend that the federal government has not taken an active role in physically restoring the Sea.[92] Most federal actions have centered on creating proposals for restoration and conducting pilot studies. Restoration efforts have largely centered on state actions. Congress might consider shifting the federal position to a more active role by authorizing federal restoration actions and providing appropriations to implement them. In contrast, Congress might consider leaving restoration responsibilities to the State of California and allowing the federal government to continue its supporting role.

The importance of the decision of how to proceed might amplify as the QSA goes into effect and temporary local mitigation efforts end. The presence of endangered species in the Salton Sea and documented health hazards from the evaporation of the Sea are issues some cite to justify federal action. The following section provides an overview of the issues concerning the federal role in restoring the Salton Sea, and then discusses specific aspects of the federal role and how Congress might address them.

Is There a Federal Role in Restoring the Salton Sea?

Some contend that the federal government should have a greater role in restoring the Salton Sea. They note that the federal government owns 47% of the land underneath the Sea, and federal agencies, such as the Bureau of Land Management, have leased a portion of the land to private entities for oil and natural gas development. They also note that the Salton Sea ecosystem is important for several listed species under the federal ESA and that the Department of the Interior is currently conducting studies to evaluate proposals for restoring the Salton Sea. Others counter this sentiment by noting that there are no laws that authorize direct federal involvement in physically restoring the Sea. (Note that some federal laws authorizing broad restoration actions could be applied to restoring parts of the Salton Sea ecosystem.) Further, they note that the State of California is directly authorized to restore the Sea under state law and that restoration should be a state responsibility.[93] State efforts to restore the Salton Sea ecosystem have largely gone unfunded due to state fiscal concerns, according to some. Some note that if federal funds were available, the construction and development of larger restoration projects could proceed.

Due to the expense and estimated costs of currently proposed restoration plans, advocates argue that a combined state and federal effort to restore the Salton Sea would be an appropriately balanced approach to restoration. However, some may contend that an open-ended federal commitment to restore an area with questionable prospects for restoration success may not be the best use of federal resources in a time of fiscal constraint. They contend that other wetland restoration efforts, such as in the San Francisco Bay and Sacramento and San Joaquin Rivers Delta (Bay-Delta) and Lake Tahoe in

California would be more cost-effective and efficient ways to address species concerns and restore existing ecosystems.[94]

If Congress considers expanding the federal role in restoring the Salton Sea, there are a few factors to consider, including (1) creating authorizing legislation to create a comprehensive plan (or implement an existing plan) and governance structure for restoration; (2) funding existing authorized activities or a new effort at restoration; (3) addressing restoration under ESA; and (4) maintaining the status quo of providing assistance to the State of California. Lastly, Congress might decide not to address restoration in the Salton Sea ecosystem. If Congress chooses not to authorize or fund Salton Sea restoration activities, efforts by the State of California would be the primary avenue for restoration. California is directed under the QSA and the state law to mitigate the effects of the QSA in the Salton Sea. However, even with mitigating the effects of the QSA, habitat loss and salinity is expected to continue.[95] The next sections discuss options for Congress listed above.

Comprehensive Plan and Governance for Restoration

The Salton Sea does not have a comprehensive plan that is being implemented for restoration. Several entities have released different restoration plans. Many state, tribal, and federal agencies have a stake in the Basin and each has proposed different plans. The current proposed state plan is estimated to cost $8.9 billion. The federal restoration alternatives identified by BOR in 2007 had estimated costs ranging from $3.5 billion to $14 billion.[96] So far, state and federal appropriations have not been provided to support the implementation of any large-scale project. Some private stakeholders have presented smaller-scale versions of the state and federal plans that cut costs by eliminating certain aspects of the plans. These partial restoration plans are estimated to reduce costs by up to 75%.[97]

Most of the funding for restoring the Salton Sea, according to some, has been spent on creating plans and monitoring, rather than directly implementing projects.[98] These studies have provided data and highlighted issues and strategies for future restoration projects. However, the short lifespan (most projects are decommissioned within five years) of these efforts may result in limited long-term environmental impacts.

Congress might consider increasing the federal role in restoring the Salton Sea by authorizing the creation of a comprehensive restoration plan that would involve federal and state resources and incorporate shared governance, or authorizing an existing proposed restoration plan. For example, restoration in the Greater Florida Everglades is guided by the Comprehensive Everglades Restoration Plan (CERP), which includes 68 projects and has a 1:1 cost share between the federal government and the State of Florida.[99] DOI and the Corps are the primary federal entities involved and the South Florida Water Management District is the non-federal sponsor. Other ecosystem restoration initiatives in areas such as the Chesapeake Bay and Platte River also involve the federal government and one or more states. An alternative to creating and authorizing a comprehensive plan for restoration could be to expand and fund existing federal authorities that contribute toward restoring the Salton Sea.

Funding

Congress may choose to expand the federal role in the restoration of the Salton Sea by funding existing restoration projects and authorizations aimed at restoration. For example, the Water Resources Development Act of 2007 authorized the Secretary of the Army to review the state plan and determine whether pilot projects in the plan are feasible. If the Secretary decides that the projects are feasible, then he is authorized to enter into an agreement with the state, in consultation with the Salton Sea Authority and the Salton Sea Science Office, to carry out the pilot projects. The non-federal sponsor (e.g., State of California) would pay 35% of the total cost of the project, and the federal government would pay 65%. The law authorizes $30 million for these projects, with no more than $5 million per project. To date, no funding has been authorized for the Corps to carry out these projects; however, the Administration has requested $200,000 for a reconnaissance study on these pilot projects for FY2014.[100]

Other federal authorities for addressing restoration in the Salton Sea are primarily for conducting studies to determine if certain restoration methods are feasible. For example, funds authorized by the Salton Sea Reclamation Act of 1998 (P.L. 105-372) are for implementing pilot projects to measure saline habitat pools. BOR received appropriations (and then contracted with USGS) to carry out these pilot studies and have reported generally positive results. Funding has also been used to implement scientific research on the Salton Sea as well as monitoring and collecting data about the state of the Sea.

Some programs under ESA could be applied to restoration of habitat and species recovery and used to help fund efforts in the Salton Basin. The Salton Sea is a key stop along the Pacific Flyway, which serves as the migratory route for many endangered and threatened species. The Salton Sea is not currently designated as critical habitat for these species, which has been questioned by some scientists who believe it should be listed as critical habitat along the Flyway. Nearby areas, however, do contain critical habitat and can play a role in restoration. For example, parts of the Imperial Valley, including the Salton Sea, were designated a critical habitat for the desert pupfish.[101] The recovery plan for the desert pupfish states that the few natural habitats and populations remaining should be protected.[102] The incidental take permits granted by the Fish and Wildlife Service for the water transfer authorized under the QSA require that the participating parties maintain desert pupfish habitat connectivity. Further, QSA mitigation requires that desert pupfish habitats be maintained as long as the transfers are occurring and that a detailed management plan be developed when salinity reaches 90 ppt (the point at which desert pupfish can no longer reproduce in the Sea).[103] These requirements might stimulate restoration and maintenance of the Salton Sea or the maintenance of small habitat pools to maintain these endangered species.

Possible funding sources through the ESA include appropriations for recovery actions of listed species and the Cooperative Endangered Species Conservation Fund (CESCF). CESCF could benefit species that are listed or proposed for listing under ESA, through grants to states and territories. Funds from CESCF could also be used to help states prepare Habitat Conservation Plans (HCPs). If there are several actors participating in the creation of an HCP, states can use their funds to coordinate the effort and develop a single plan that might cover the region.

Some alternative funding mechanisms have been proposed by state, local, and private entities that could involve the federal government. For example, some have proposed the use of renewable energy development in the Basin to help fund restoration. One way to utilize renewable energy would be through public-private partnerships (PPPs). PPPs involve contract arrangements in which a nonfederal or private entity partners with the government to contribute funds, knowledge, or labor toward a project. In return, the private or nonfederal entity is guaranteed a portion of the project's revenue as repayment. The other portion of the revenue could be used to fund public goods such as restoration. Multiple federal agencies have instituted public-private programs to fund and manage restoration. These include the National Oceanic and Atmospheric Administration (NOAA), the U.S. Army Corps of Engineers (Corps), the Bureau of Land Management (BLM), the U.S. Forest Service (USFS), and the Fish and Wildlife Service (FWS), among others. Many of these agencies have programs that provide funding for a project while a private company develops and constructs the project. In several cases, this model also involves cost-sharing between the federal agency and nonfederal entity.

According to independent studies commissioned by stakeholders in the area, the Salton Sea Basin has large renewable energy potential.[104] This includes geothermal, solar, and bio-algae energy production. Integrating energy production and PPPs to generate funds for restoration has been suggested by some as a potential alternative to raise revenue and improve the local economy in the Basin. Potential federal entities that could be involved with PPPs in the area include BLM and FWS. However, for PPPs to be viable, they would need to generate revenues with minimal risk to the private entity. Some contend that the barriers to renewable energy development in Salton Sea Basin, such as lack of access to transmission lines, lack of access to water necessary to run generators, and environmental concerns including endangered species and seismic inductions due to the activities, might be prohibitive for energy development in the area.[105]

What if No Restoration Occurs?

Congress might consider the potential effects of not restoring the Salton Sea in weighing options for action. Most studies and statements by scientists and other stakeholders note that the Sea will shrink in size and increase in salinity without restoration. This is expected to amplify after 2018, which is the expected date for mitigation deliveries to the Salton Sea to stop under the QSA.[106] Some have modeled the future physical characteristics of the Salton Sea without restoration.[107] Without restoration, the present ecosystem would be unable to continue with high salinity concentrations. The migratory birds that visit the Salton Sea would largely disappear from the area.[108] The Salton Basin, however, could still be ecologically productive. For example, the high salinity concentrations would be conducive for brine shrimp, flies, algae, and bacteria. Over time, however, the salinity and oxygen depletion could reach levels that would affect the survival of remaining organisms in the area. While modeling has predicted that the sea size would stabilize around 2040, the salinity would continue to increase. Models estimate that salinity would be 330 ppt by 2075. To put this in perspective, the saltiest portions of the Great Salt Lake in Utah are 270 ppt and the Dead Sea is around 337 ppt.

By 2040, an additional 134 square miles of the seabed would be exposed compared to the present size of the Sea. Contaminated dust from these exposed areas could impact the livelihood of the farmers in the surrounding counties and have adverse health effects on those in neighboring communities. Studies have not been able to quantify the economic impacts of increasing dust on the agricultural economy in the area. However, possible impacts include damaged crops and additional water needed to leech salts and toxins from the soil. Many of the business owners in the area have stated that lack of restoration would lead businesses in the area to close. Locals have expressed fears that unemployment would increase if businesses closed. Also, the state and federal governments may bear additional health care costs due to increased health problems.[109]

While acknowledging that the Salton Sea ecosystem is undergoing a transition to a smaller and saltier water body, some contend that the natural transition of the Sea should not be interfered with. These opponents of restoration contend that the future Salton Sea will have a new, but equally productive, ecosystem that better fits with the physical and chemical properties of the Sea. They believe that restoring the Sea should not be a priority. Others counter this sentiment by noting the severity of the projected effects of a shrinking sea on the environment and economy of the region.

Understanding the science behind the ecosystem dynamics in the Salton Sea Basin is viewed as a priority by some who contend that long-term monitoring of the Salton Sea ecosystem is essential for deciding whether to restore the Sea or let it transition into a new ecosystem. The USGS and BOR collaborated with the California Department of Water Resources and Fish and Wildlife to create a Monitoring and Assessment Plan (MAP).[110] This plan would implement a monitoring program that would establish a baseline understanding of the key factors in the Salton Sea ecosystem (e.g, salinity and area of exposed seabed, among others); fill in data gaps; and provide capacity for storing, managing, and analyzing data. The program is not intended to be a prescriptive plan for restoration, but rather aims to implement monitoring activities directed at species and habitats that could be affected by future restoration activities.

CONCLUSION

The Salton Sea ecosystem has been steadily changing primarily due to less water entering the Sea. The notable changes are the decreasing area of the Salton Sea and increasing salinity of its waters. These changes have already caused stress on fish and wildlife species that reside in the ecosystem, and some avian species that use the ecosystem while migrating along the Pacific Flyway. The condition of the Salton Sea ecosystem is expected to change dramatically when water transfers authorized under QSA are implemented, thus reducing water inflows into the Sea. This is expected to increase the level of salinity in the Sea over a short period, thus making the Sea inhabitable for most existing fish and wildlife species. Severe effects on the ecosystem are expected as soon as 2018, according to some models.

Several groups support restoring the Salton Sea ecosystem so that it can support fish and wildlife and stimulate economic development in the region. Specifically, proponents of restoring the Sea base their arguments on the value of the Salton Sea as one of the few remaining habitats in the region for migratory birds and other fish and wildlife. They note that with nearly 90% of California's original wetlands gone, the Sea is of regional or national importance to pelicans and cormorants, wading birds, waterfowl, shorebirds, gulls, and terns.[111] Further, some note that a restored Sea could supports aquatic wildlife that include some threatened and endangered species and other species that might be able to support recreational or sport fishing practices. The value of a restored Sea, according to some, can also be measured in terms of its potential for recreation and economic development (e.g., tourism) as well as its function for agricultural drainage.

Some opposed to restoring the Salton Sea base their arguments on the premise that the Salton Sea is destined to evaporate and eventually convert back to a desert ecosystem. Throughout geologic history, water bodies in the Salton Basin have eventually dried up, leading some scientists to hypothesize that evaporation and conversion to a salt brine would be the progression of the Salton Sea if no restoration activities are undertaken. Some critics also argue that salinity levels will increase in the Sea despite restoration attempts, especially if water inflows to the Sea are reduced by water transfers or other water diversions away from the sea.[112] Further, without the ability to use fresh water from the Colorado River, many of the restoration plans and projects developed in the early 2000s may be infeasible. As noted earlier, some argue that the high cost of restoration and the scientific uncertainty of existing proposals might not warrant limited state and federal funds. They note that limited funds should be funneled to other restoration efforts in naturally occurring wetlands in the California San Francisco Bay Sacramento/San Joaquin Rivers Delta. Congress has addressed the restoration of the Salton Sea ecosystem through various laws that authorize, in part, the creation of restoration plans for the ecosystem and the testing of restoration methodologies through pilot projects. However, due to the pace of change in the Salton Sea and the anticipation of severe effects on the ecosystem due to water transfers, Congress may decide to address restoration by increasing the federal role in restoration efforts. This could be done by funding existing federal authorities that address, or could address, restoring the ecosystem; authorizing federal participation and appropriations for implementing existing restoration plans; and authorizing a new comprehensive plan to be created that might involve participation from federal and non-federal stakeholders, similar to other restoration initiatives around the country. Congress might also decide not to address restoration of the Salton Sea ecosystem, or, rather, maintain the status quo of federal participation.

APPENDIX. CHRONOLOGY OF FEDERAL MANAGEMENT AND RESTORATION ACTIVITIES IN AND AROUND THE SALTON SEA

Year	Purpose
10,000 BC	Native Americans first occupy the Salton Basin.
700 AD	Lake Cahuilla is formed in the Salton Basin and proceeds to dry out and fill up four times.
1500 (about)	Large inflow of water fills the Salton Basin from the Gulf of California. It is 26 times the size of the Salton Sea.
1840 - 1870	Flooding from the Colorado River is recorded in the Salton Basin.
1876	U.S. Government establishes the Torres-Martinez Desert Cahuilla Indian Reservation with a grant of 640 acres.
1891	20,000 acres of land on the northern side of the Salton Basin are provided to the Torres- Martinez Band of Desert Cahuilla Indians.
1901	Imperial Canal brings water from the Colorado River to the Imperial Valley.
1905	The Salton Sea is created in the Salton Basin by a levee break in the Colorado River.
1909	The U.S. government reserves in trust nearly 10,000 acres of land under the sea for the benefit of the Torres-Martinez Indians.
1924	President Calvin Coolidge issues Public Water Reserve Order 90 (issued in 1924) and 114 (issued in 1928) setting aside lands under the Salton Sea as a permanent drainage reservoir for agricultural and surface water runoff from the Imperial and Coachella Valleys.
1928	Boulder Canyon Project Act (P.L. 70-642) authorizes the construction of the Boulder Dam and All American Canal (expected to control the Colorado River and stop flooding).
1930	Salton Sea Wildlife Refuge is established. It covers an area of 35,000 acres.[113]

Year	Purpose
1967	The yuma clapper rail is listed as an endangered species in the U.S. Its range includes the Salton Sea.
1969	A federal-state Reconnaissance Investigation studies water quality problems in the Salton Sea. Based on this study, a feasibility study of management plans is authorized in 1972.
1970	The brown pelican was listed as an endangered species. Its range includes the Salton Sea. (In 1985, the species was delisted in the East, but it is still being monitored.)
1974	Federal-state Feasibility Study, which provided alternatives for lowering the salinity and maintaining water levels in the Salton Sea, is completed.
1986	The desert pupfish is listed as a federally endangered species in its entire range, which includes the Salton Sea. A FWS Biological Opinion states that both agricultural drain maintenance activities and the introduction of sterile grass carp would not jeopardize the continued existence of desert pupfish. The Opinion allowed for unlimited incidental take of the species during drain maintenance.
1992	A second Biological Opinion for the desert pupfish, gave the same conclusion as the first with respect to agricultural drainage, but allows for only a limited take of species during drain maintenance. This Opinion also covered the yuma clapper rail and the brown pelican. 150,000 eared grebes die garnering national attention for the Salton Sea. Cause of their deaths is unknown. Title XI of the Reclamation Projects Authorization and Adjustment Act of 1992 (P.L. 102-575) authorizes research on methods to control salinity levels, provide habitat to endangered species, enhance fisheries, and protect recreational values. $10 million is authorized for this effort.
1993	The Salton Sea Authority is formed among Riverside and Imperial counties, and the Coachella Valley Water District and Imperial Irrigation District. The goal is to coordinate activities that relate to improving water quality, stabilizing water levels, and enhancing economic and recreational activities in and around the Salton Sea.
1998	The Salton Sea Reclamation Act of 1998 (P.L. 105-372) authorizes the Secretary of the Interior to complete studies of management options to allow the use of the Salton Sea to continue, and stabilize salinity and surface elevation, as well as maintain fish and wildlife populations and enhance the potential for recreation and economic development.
1999	Water Resources Development Act of 1999 (P.L. 106-53) authorizes Secretary of the Army to provide technical assistance to federal, state and local agencies to implement restoration measures in the Salton Sea, and to determine a plan in which the U.S. Army Corps of Engineers could assist others in restoring the Salton Sea.

Appendix. (Continued)

Year	Purpose
2000	The Department of the Interior submitted a Draft Environmental Impact Statement/ Environmental Impact Report, and Strategic Science Plan for restoring the Salton Sea. The USGS Salton Sea Science Office was established by DOI to provide continuity of the science effort, effectiveness of science undertaken in support of the restoration project, and efficiency of operations in serving management needs. Title VI of the Torres-Martinez Settlement Act (P.L. 106-568) provides compensation to the Torres-Martinez Desert Cahuila Indians for their submerged land. A total of $14 million was authorized, $10 million from the federal government and $4 million from water districts.
2003	Bureau of Reclamation (BOR) submits the Salton Sea Study Status Report, which contains various proposals for the full or partial restoration of the Salton Sea. Amendment to P.L. 105-372 changes the authorized appropriations for water reclamation and irrigation drainage in the New and Alamo Rivers from $3 million to $10 million.
2004	Water Supply, Reliability, and environmental Improvement Act (P.L. 108-361) requires the Secretary of the Interior to complete a feasibility study on a preferred alternative for Salton Sea restoration.
2006	Shallow Habitat Pools (SHPs) are constructed on the southern end of the Sea by BOR and US Geological Survey.
2007	Water Resources Development Act of 2007 (P.L. 110-114) authorizes $30 million for Salton Sea Restoration. Restoration of Salton Sea released by BOR and Department of Interior (DOI).
2009	Saline Habitat Complexes in the southern end are decommissioned. An Ecological Risk Assessment is published recommending SHCs.
2013	The Final EIR/EIS for the Salton Sea Species Conservation Project is released by the Corps, in conjunction with state agencies.

Federal Appropriations

Year	Funds Appropriated (Dollars, in thousands)	Purpose
1985	2,600	The Salton Sea is studied under the National Irrigation Water Quality Program (NIWQP)[114] to identify the nature and extent of irrigation-induced water quality problems from 1985 to 2003. Studies were conducted by the BOR, USFWS, and USGS.

Year	Funds Appropriated (Dollars, in thousands)	Purpose
1994 - 1996	100 (each year)	P.L. 102-575 appropriates for research on the restoration of the Salton Sea are provided.
1997	200	Same as above.
1998	400	Same as above.
	900	U.S. Environmental Protection Agency Office of Research and Development implements a Salton Sea Database Program at the University of Redlands, CA.
1999	1,000	U.S. Fish and Wildlife Service develops management options to mitigate bird die-offs in and around the Salton Sea National Wildlife Refuge.
	4,000	U.S. Environmental Protection Agency (USEPA) under P.L. 105-372 grants funds to the Salton Sea Authority to research water quality and wildlife in and around the Salton Sea.[115]
	3,000	Title II of P.L. 105-372 appropriated through the USEPA funds demonstration wetland projects on the New and Alamo Rivers.
	2,800	USEPA Office of Research and Development funds Salton Sea database program.
	1,000	U.S. Fish and Wildlife Service develops management options to mitigate bird die-offs in and around the Salton Sea National Wildlife Refuge.
2000	1,000	P.L. 105-372 funds for Salton Sea Research Project through the Bureau of Reclamation (BOR)
	1,000	U.S. Fish and Wildlife Service develops management options to mitigate bird die-offs in and around the Salton Sea National Wildlife Refuge.
2001	5,000	P.L. 105-372 funds for Salton Sea Research Project, BOR.
	1,000	Salton Sea Recovery Program activities in the Salton Sea National Wildlife Refuge by the U.S. Fish and Wildlife Service
2002	4,500	Salton Sea restoration activities and reclamation of the New and Alamo Rivers through BOR. Funds from P.L. 105-372 and P.L. 102-575.
	1,000	Salton Sea Recovery Program activities in the Salton Sea National Wildlife Refuge by the U.S. Fish and Wildlife Service.
2003	2,000	Salton Sea Research Project funded by from Consolidated Appropriations Resolution FY2003 (P.L. 108-7).
	1,000	Salton Sea Recovery Program activities in the Salton Sea National Wildlife Refuge by U.S. Fish and Wildlife Service.

(Continued)

Year	Funds Appropriated (Dollars, in thousands)	Purpose
	4,000	Energy and Water Development Appropriations for FY2004 (P.L. 108-137) provides appropriations for desalinization studies, restoration activities in the New and Alamo Rivers, groundwater assessment, and programs conducted by the Salton Sea Authority.
2004	3,595	P.L. 105-372 funds for Salton Sea Research Project, BOR.
2005	1,994	P.L. 105-372 funds for Salton Sea Research Project, BOR.
2006	4,780	P.L. 105-372 funds for Salton Sea Research Project, BOR.
2007	743	P.L. 105-372 funds for Salton Sea Research Project, BOR.
2008	1,132	P.L. 105-372 funds for Salton Sea Research Project, BOR.
2009	1,074	P.L. 105-372 funds for Salton Sea Research Project, BOR.
2010	379	P.L. 105-372 funds for Salton Sea Research Project, BOR.
2011	400	P.L. 105-372 funds for Salton Sea Research Project, BOR.
2012	290	P.L. 105-372 funds for Salton Sea Research Project, BOR.
2013	300	BOR Salton Sea Research Project funded by Continued Appropriations (P.L. 112-175).
Total	**51,387**	

Sources: Cohen et al., *Haven or Hazard*, 63 p; U.S. Dept. of Interior, *Budget Justifications for FY 2000-2013*; U.S. Dept. of the Interior, *Saving the Salton Sea: A Research Needs Assessment*, Proceedings from the Workshop held August 4 - 8, 1997, Palm Springs, CA; Phone conversation with Clark Newby, Bureau of Reclamation Budget Office, on February 12, 2003; U.S. House of Representatives, Committee on Resources, Subcommittee on Water and Power, *Salton Sea Stabilization and Water Quality Improvement*, Oversight Hearing, 105th Congress, 1st session (Serial No. 105-60), October 3, 1997 (Washington, DC: GPO), 112 p.; and various other sources.

End Notes

[1] U.S. House of Representatives, Committee on Resources, Subcommittee on Water and Power, *H.R. 5123, The Colorado River Quantification Settlement Facilitation Act*, Hearing, 107th Cong., 2nd Sess., July 25, 2002, (Washington, DC: GPO).

[2] Michael J. Cohen and Karen H. Hyun, HAZARD: *The Future of the Salton Sea With No Restoration Project*, Pacific Institute, May 2006, http://www.pacinst.org/wp-content/ uploads/2013/02/report15.pdf.

[3] Imperial Irrigation District, Metropolitan Water District of Southern California, and Coachella Valley Water District. *The Quantification Settlement Agreement and Related Agreements*

and Documents, October 10, 2003, http://www.sdcwa.org/sites/default/files/files/QSA_ final.pdf.

[4] Letters to Secretary of the Interior Gale Norton from Congressman Duncan Hunter on December 19, 2002, and Senator Dianne Feinstein and Congresswoman Mary Bono on January 31, 2003.

[5] Lisa Lien-Mager, *Lawmakers Call for Action on Salton Sea*, Association of California Water Agencies, September 19, 2012, http://www.acwa.com/news/water-news/lawmakers-call-action-salton-sea.

[6] P.L. 110-114, Section 3032.

[7] Michelle Nijhunis, "Accidental refuge: Should we save the Salton Sea?," *High Country News*. http://www.hcn.org/issues/181/5865/print_view.

[8] Robert H. Boyle, "Life—or Death—for the Salton Sea?" *Smithsonian* (June 1996): 87-93. (Hereinafter referred to as Boyle, "Life—or Death—for the Salton Sea?")

[9] Chelsea Congdon, Kathrine Currie, and Taylor Miller, et al., *Summary analysis of authorities and responsibilities associated with the Salton Sea*, San Diego State University, July 1988, http://www.sci.sdsu.edu/salton/ MeyersResSSAppendixF.html.

[10] Cohen et al., *Haven or Hazard*. p. 10.

[11] California Department of Water Resources and California Department of Fish and Gamer, *Salton Sea Species Conservation Habitat Project Draft Environmental Impact Statement*, August 2011, http://www.water.ca.gov/saltonsea/ habitat/eir2011.cfm. (Hereinafter referred to as *SCH Project EIS/EIR*.)

[12] Anoxic waters refer to waters with a total depletion of oxygen, an extreme version of hypoxia. Fish need oxygenated waters to survive, thus anoxic conditions is often associated with large fish kills, sometimes observed in the Salton Sea. See B. Marti-Cardona et al., "Relating Fish Kills to Upwelling and Wind Patterns in the Salton Sea," in *Developments in Hydrobiology: The Salton Sea Centennial Symposium Developments in Hydrobiology*, ed. Stuart Hurlbert, vol. 201 (2008), pp. 85-95.

[13] Cohen et al., *Haven or Hazard*, p. 9.

[14] W.A. Dill and A.J. Cordone, *History and Status of Introduced Fishes in California*, 1871-1996, California Department of Fish and Game Fisheries Bulletin 178 (Sacramento, CA: 1997), p. 414.

[15] *SCH Project EIS/EIR*. Section 1, p. 3.

[16] Michael J. Cohen and Karen H. Hyun, HAZARD: *The Future of the Salton Sea With No Restoration Project*, Pacific Institute, May 2006, http://www.pacinst.org/wp-content/ uploads/2013/02/report15.pdf.

[17] Ann Vilesis, *Discovering the Unknown Landscape: A History of America's Wetlands* (Covelo, CA: Island Press, 1997).

[18] 16 U.S.C. Chapter 35, Section 1531-1544.

[19] Jeanie Jones, P.E., "Management of the Salton Sea Ecosystem," *Southwest Hydrology*, July/August 2004.

[20] W.D. Shuford, N. Warnock, K.C. Molina, and K.K. Sturm, "The Salton Sea as Critical Habitat to Migratory and Resident Waterbirds," *Hydrobiologia* 473 (2002): p. 255-274.

[21] For more information on the Salton Sea Authority, see http://saltonsea.ca.gov/.

[22] Salton Sea Authority, *Salton Sea Authority Plan for Multi-Purpose Project*, La Quinta, CA, June 29, 2006, http://saltonsea.ca.gov/pdfs/ssa-plan-board-review-copy-7-20-06.pdf. (Hereinafter, *2006 SSA Plan*).

[23] *2006 SSA Plan*.

[24] U.S. Bureau of Reclamation, *Restoration of the Salton Sea: Volume 1: Evaluation of Alternatives*, U.S. Bureau of Reclamation, December 2007, pp. 4-7.

[25] *2006 SSA Plan*.

[26] Jeanie Jones, P.E., "Management of the Salton Sea Ecosystem," *Southwest Hydrology*, July/August 2004.

[27] San Diego County Water Authority, *Quantification Settlement Agreement Fact Sheet*, San Diego, CA, http://www.sdcwa.org.

[28] The agreement will last for 45 years with an option to extend the transfer an additional 30 years.

[29] Currently, 100,000 AFY is transferred to SDCWA. San Diego County Water Authority, *Quantification Settlement Agreement Fact Sheet*.

[30] San Diego County Water Authority, *Quantification Settlement Agreement Fact Sheet*.

[31] Originally, IID offered to provide water until 2030. In Order WRO 2002-0013, the California State Water Resources Control Board (SWRCB) decreased this to 15 years, stating that this reduced timeframe would still prevent unreasonable environmental damage while insuring that the mitigation costs of the transfer would not be prohibitory for the stakeholders involved. SWRCB stated that those 15 years would allow the State to determine whether restoration of the Salton Sea was feasible and begin implementation of any restoration efforts. The full SWRCB Order WRO 2002-13 can be found at http://www.iid.com/ Modules/ShowDocument.aspx?documentid=924.

[32] Jeanie Jones, P.E., "Management of the Salton Sea Ecosystem," *Southwest Hydrology*, July/August 2004.

[33] SSRF is a state program funded by Prop 84, or the Safe Drinking Water, Water Quality and Supply, Flood Control, River and Coastal Protection Bond Act of 2006. This state law authorized $5.4 billion in general funds for projects pertaining to safe drinking water, water pollution control, water supply and quality, flood control, waterway and natural resources protection, state and local park improvements, and water conservation efforts. So far, the SSRF has appropriated $32 million in projects in the past 10 years.

[34] Jeanie Jones, P.E., "Management of the Salton Sea Ecosystem," *Southwest Hydrology*, July/August 2004. P. 2.

[35] Fish and Game Code Section 2081.7, subdivision (d), paragraph 3.

[36] See SB 317 (Chapter 612, Statutes of 2003).

[37] The final court ruling was released on July 31st, 2013, and found that it was within IID's authority to sign the QSA and agree to its terms, upholding the legality of the agreement. The full court case can be found at http://www.saccourt.ca.gov/coordinated-cases/qsa/ qsa.aspx.

[38] The QSA was enacted into law through a package of legislation, including SB 277 (Chapter 611, statutes of 2003); SB 317 (Chapter 612, Statutes of 2003); SB 654 (Chapter 613, Statutes of 2003); SB 1214 (Chapter 614, Statutes of 2004). In addition, the Fish and Game Code was amended to include Section 2081.7 concerning the QSA and Salton Sea mitigation requirements.

[39] The EIR only addressed the increased rate of salinization due to water transfers, accounting for increasing salinity naturally in the baseline. Therefore, mitigation activities were only designed to prevent any additional rise in salinity above the Sea's naturally increasing future salinity, not to restore the sea indefinitely or to previous, lower salinity levels. The EIR can be found at http://www.iid.com/index.aspx?page=229.

[40] See SB 654 (Machado, Chapter 613, Statutes of 2003), section 3.

[41] See SB 654 (Machado, Chapter 613, Statutes of 2003), section 3.

[42] California Department of Water Resources and Fish and Game, *Salton Sea Ecosystem Restoration Program: Preferred Alternative Report and Funding Plan*, California Resources Agency, May 2007, p. 3.

[43] R. Riedel, L. Caskey, and B.A. Costa-Pierce, "Fish Biology and Fisheries Ecology of the Salton Sea, California," *Hydrobiologia*, 473 (2002): p. 229-244.

[44] Modeling predicts that the Salton Sea would have reached 60 ppt between 2023-2030 with no water transfers.

[45] Michael J. Cohen and Karen H. Hyun, *HAZARD: The Future of the Salton Sea With No Restoration Project*, Pacific Institute, May 2006, http://www.pacinst.org/wp-content/ uploads/2013/02/report15.pdf.

[46] Boyle, "Life—or Death—for the Salton Sea?"

[47] Human exposure to DDE and Selenium comes from eating the meat of animals that lived in areas with high levels of the compounds. Public health warnings about consuming fish from the Salton Sea have been posted by the State Office of Health and Hazardous Assessment since the 1990s.

[48] DDT was banned in the United States in 1972, but is still used in Mexico as an insecticide.

[49] Dr. Tonie E. Rocke, *California's Salton Sea- A Troubled Ecosystem*, U.S. Geological Survey, June 2001, http://www.nwhc.usgs.gov/publications/fact_sheets/pdfs/fact_salton2.pdf.

[50] This was the largest die off of an endangered species at the time. For a chronology of events at Salton Sea, see http://saltonsea.ca.gov/history_chronology.html.

[51] B. Kuperman and V. Matey, *Fish Parasites of the Salton Sea*, presented at the Science for Salton Sea Ecosystem Management Conference (Riverside, CA: University of California January 5, 1999).

[52] *SCH Project EIS/EIR.*

[53] This endangered fish is only located in a few sites in the Salton Sea and the Colorado River Delta in Baja California. Imperial Irrigation District. *Habitat Conservation Plan.Ch.3. Included in the Water Conservation and Transfer Project EIR.* October 2002.

[54] *SCH Project EIS/EIR.*

[55] County of Imperial, *QSA Litigation Bulletin: Environmental Impact*, April 2009, http://www.co.imperial.ca.us/ PdfDocuments/QSALitigationBulletin.pdf.

[56] One in five children in Imperial County is asthmatic and the county has almost three times the state average of ER visits. Coachella Valley has more than three times the state average rate of asthma, with most cases concentrated in the elderly population.

[57] Rebecca Walsh, "Deadly dustbowl seen as future of Salton Sea."

[58] Rebecca Walsh, "Deadly dustbowl seen as future of Salton Sea."

[59] Dust mitigation cost estimates have been based on the actual cost of similar mitigation in Owens Lake. Owens Lake is a water body in the Sierra Nevadas. When the Owens River was diverted away from the lake in 1913, the lake began to dry up. Today it is almost completely dry. Owens Lake is currently the largest single source of dust pollution in the nation. Ian James, "Engineer sees big challenges saving the Salton Sea," *The Desert Sun*, April 13, 2013.

[60] Keith Matheny, "Officials, activists push for fix to Salton Sea's growing crisis," *The Desert Sun*, December 19, 2012.

[61] $200,000 was appropriated. Janet Zimmerman, "Salton Sea: $200,000 Ok'd to monitor for odors," *The Press Enterprise*, January 4, 2013. http://www.pe.com/local-news/local-news-headlines/20130104-region-salton-sea-to-get- air-monitoring-for-odors.ece.

[62] The measurements of hydrogen sulfide were one-tenth to one-millionth the level at which the odor would be considered a risk to public health.

[63] This act was enacted after a die-off of eared grebes (approximately 150,000 birds were found dead).

[64] This includes studies on the effects of selenium and high salinity on species in the area.

[65] See Salton Sea Salinity Control Research Project.

[66] This would have separated the Sea into two basins, an 85,000 acre North Basin that would reach salinity levels similar to the ocean, and a southern section that would consist of wetlands areas as well as numerous recreational lakes ranging from fresh water to hyper saline. Plan available at http://saltonsea.ca.gov/media/ppr_summary.pdf.

[67] Plan available at http://saltonsea.ca.gov/pdfs/ssa-plan-board-review-copy-7-20-06.pdf.

[68] QSA Coordinated Special Proceedings are filed under case number JCCP 4353 (there have been nine separate cases filed; cases were first heard by Imperial County until 2008 and then appealed to Sacramento County).. For discussion of QSA's effect on restoration possibilities, see Bureau of Reclamation's 2007 *Restoration of the Salton Sea Summary Report* (p. xx) and Salton Sea Ecosystem Monitoring Project (p. 4) as examples.

[69] Section 101(b)(2)(C)(i) of P.L. 105-372.

[70] The full plan can be found at http://www.water.ca.gov/saltonsea/docs/Funding_Plan.pdf.

[71] These components would be created by beams and rock barriers. Construction is estimated to take 70 years; in total, 62,000 acres of Saline Habitat Complex, 45,000 acres of marine sea, 106,000 acres of exposed playas including geothermal areas, and 75,000 acres designated as an air quality management area would exist in the Salton Basin after construction. There would also be two sedimentation/distribution basins.

[72] The cost figure does not include the cost of the Demonstration Project ($6.6 million), investigations in addition to pre-design efforts and administrative costs pre-construction ($19.3 million), permits/land or easement acquisitions (~$10 million), or interest on borrowed funds.

[73] The Final ESI/EIR for the plan is available at http://www.water.ca.gov/saltonsea/habitat/eir2013.cfm.

[74] The Final ESI/EIR for the plan is available at http://www.water.ca.gov/saltonsea/habitat/eir2013.cfm.

[75] These negotiations were held in May 2013, ending with an agreement between IID, County of Imperial, and the Imperial County Air Pollution Control District to pursue funding for restoration, including the use of geothermal and other renewable energy in the Salton Basin to provide long-term funding. The terms of agreement included the endorsement of the 2006 *SSA Plan*, as well as increased geothermal capacity of 1,400 megawatts (MW) (up from 600 MW) and a surcharge at Hoover Dam to pay for restoration of the Salton Sea, among other things. Full terms can be found at http://www.iid.com/modules/showdocument.aspx?documentid=7818.

[76] For the text of AB71 and its status, see http://leginfo.legislature.ca.gov/faces/billNavClient.xhtml?bill_id=201320140AB71

[77] Full study available at http://www.usbr.gov/lc/region/saltnsea/finalreport/index.html.

[78] Cost in 2006 dollars. The no action alternative was estimated to cost $1 billion for dust mitigation. From Bureau of Reclamation, *Budget Justification for FY 2009*, http://www.doi.gov/budget/appropriations/2009/upload/BOR-Budget- Justification.pdf.

[79] Report and findings found in: A. Keith Miles, Mark A. Ricca, and Anne Meckstroth, et al., *Salton Sea Ecosystem Monitoring Project*, USGS and US DOI, Open File Report 2009-1276, Reston, VA, 2009, http://www.usbr.gov/lc/region/saltnsea/SaltonSeaEcosystem Monitoring.pdf.

[80] Ibid, p. 29.

[81] Section 3032. The pilot project the secretary is currently studying is termed the Salton Sea Species Conservation Habitat Project. (This is discussed in greater detail under the State Actions section below.)

[82] Section 3032.

[83] Army Corps of Engineers, *Civil Works Budget FY* 2014, 2013, http://cdm16021.contentdm.oclc.org/cdm/ref/collection/p16021coll6/id/42.

[84] See AB 148 from the 2013-2014 California legislative session.

[85] Summit Blue Consulting LLC, *Renewable Energy Feasibility Study Final Report*, Imperial Irrigation District, April 1, 2008.

[86] See the Imperial Irrigation District Resolution No. 14-2013 (Geothermal Energy Development and Use). http://www.iid.com/Modules/ShowDocument.aspx?documentid=7742.

[87] Details of the projects can be found through the Salton Sea Financial Assistance Program at http://www.water.ca.gov/saltonsea/habitat/final_list.cfm.

[88] Keith Matheny, "Officials, activists push for fix to the Salton Sea's growing crisis," *The Desert Sun*, December 19, 2012.

[89] D.E. Brune, H.W. Yen, and G. Schwartz, et al., "The Controlled Eutrophication Process; Microalgae for Biofuels Production and Fertilizer" (Clemson University).

[90] Ibid.

[91] Michelle Nijhunis, "Accidental refuge: Should we save the Salton Sea?," *High Country News*. http://www.hcn.org/issues/181/5865/print_view.

[92] Keith Matheny, "Officials, activists push for fix to Salton Sea's growing crisis," *The Desert Sun*, December 19, 2012.

[93] See SB 654 (Machado, Chapter 613, Statutes of 2003), section 2.

[94] Michelle Nijhunis, "Accidental refuge: Should we save the Salton Sea?," *High Country News*. http://www.hcn.org/issues/181/5865/print_view.

[95] State Water Resources Control Board, *Order WRO 2003-0013*, 2003. http://www.iid.com/Modules/ShowDocument.aspx?documentid=924.

[96] Bureau of Reclamation, *Restoration of the Salton Sea Summary Report*, September 2007, http://www.usbr.gov/lc/region/saltnsea/FinalSummaryRpt.pdf.

[97] See Michael Cohen's Restoration Plan as an example. Information available at http://www.pacinst.org/about-us/staff- and-board/michael-j-cohen/.

[98] Michael Cohen, *State Not Meeting Salton Sea Responsibilities*, Pacific Institute, October 10, 2009, http://www.pacinst.org/publication/state-not-meeting-salton-sea-responsibilities/.

[99] CRS Report R42007, Everglades Restoration: *Federal Funding and Implementation Progress*, by Charles V. Stern

[100] Army Corps of Engineers, *Civil Works Budget FY 2014*, 2013, http://cdm16021.contentdm.oclc.org/cdm/ref/collection/p16021coll6/id/42.

[101] The FWS last reviewed the pupfish in 2010, and determined that the pupfish should still be listed due to little population growth and increasing threats to the pupfish habitat. Although their numbers are low, recovery could potentially be large. For example, the desert pupfish were barred from experimental pools in the Salton Sea created by USGS and BOR. A small number infiltrated the study pools when they were completed in 2006. By 2010, over 1 million pupfish were found in the pools, indicating the potential for recovery using the pools. For more, see US Fish and Wildlife Service, *Biological Opinion for the Salton Sea Species Conservation Habitat Project*, March 5, 2013, http://criticalhabitat.fws.gov/docs/tails/11430/v699163.pdf.

[102] The recovery plan is available at http://www.fws.gov/carlsbad/speciesstatuslist/ rp/19931208_rp_depu.pdf.

[103] Bureau of Reclamation, Conservation Agreement among Bureau of Reclamation, Imperial Irrigation District, Coachella Valley Water District, and San Diego County Water Authority, October 10, 2003, http://www.iid.com/Modules/ShowDocument.aspx?documentid=4594.

[104] Summit Blue Consulting LLC, *Renewable Energy Feasibility Study Final Report*, Imperial Irrigation District, April 1, 2008.

[105] See Summit Blue Consulting LLC, *Renewable Energy Feasibility Study Final Report*, Imperial Irrigation District, April 1, 2008, for complete list of potential barriers and additional details.

[106] Michael J. Cohen and Karen H. Hyun, HAZARD: *The Future of the Salton Sea With No Restoration Project*, Pacific Institute, May 2006, http://www.pacinst.org/wp-content/uploads/2013/02/report15.pdf.

[107] While this section draws mainly off of one study conducted by the Pacific Institute due to its recent publication, the findings are similar to many of the predictions about the future state of the Salton Sea scientific papers from the 1980s and 1990s.

[108] Fish and Wildlife Service's Biological Opinion for the QSA estimated that once salinity in the Sea reached 60 ppt, only 25 pelicans would remain in the Basin. It was estimated that the first 45 years of the water transfers would cause 12,383 lost pelican-use years. To account for this, two roosts for brown pelicans are to be established in San Diego and Santa Barbara that can hold 1,200 pelicans by 2018. The Biological Opinion can be found at http://www.iid.com/ Modules/ShowDocument.aspx?documentid=2263.

[109] High cases of liver, kidney, and respiratory diseases have been reported in areas that have experienced similar shrinking lakes (e.g. Aral Lake and Owens Lake). The United Nations has reported an increase in immune-system disorders, birth abnormalities, tuberculosis, and

cancer rates in the Aral Sea area since the Sea began shrinking; it has been, at least, partially attributed to the increased dust from the exposed seabed.

[110] H.L. Case III, Jerry Boles, and Arturo Delgado, *Salton Sea Ecosystem Monitoring and Assessment Plan*, U.S. Geological Survey, Open-File Report 2013-1133, Reston, VA, August 20, 2013, http://pubs.usgs.gov/of/2013/1133/ pdf/ofr20131133.pdf.

[111] W.D. Shuford, N. Warnock, K.C. Molina, and K.K. Sturm, "The Salton Sea as Critical Habitat to Migratory and Resident Waterbirds," *Hydrobiologia* 473 (2002), p. 255-274.

[112] According to the BOR, water use in Mexican urban areas on the border may increase if water quality is improved. This may lower water inflows in the New River and hence reduce water flowing into the Salton Sea.

[113] Due to flooding and a rise in sea level since 1930, only 2,000 acres remain uncovered by salty water. The refuge was renamed to Sonny Bono Salton Sea National Wildlife Refuge in 1998. See U.S. Fish and Wildlife Service, Pacific Region at http://www.fws.gov/refuge/ sonny_bono_salton_sea/.

[114] This is a cooperative program among the U.S. Geological Survey, U.S. Fish and Wildlife Service, and the Bureau of Reclamation. The effects of chemicals such as selenium, boron, and DDE were investigated in wildlife in and around the Salton Sea.

[115] This funding was provided in research grants to various public and private institutions. The USGS conducted studies on microbial pathogens and causes of the mortality of eared grebes in the Salton Sea.

In: Ecosystem Restoration
Editor: Simon Acheson

ISBN: 978-1-63117-540-4
© 2014 Nova Science Publishers, Inc.

Chapter 3

THE GREAT LAKES RESTORATION INITIATIVE: BACKGROUND AND ISSUES[*]

Pervaze A. Sheikh

SUMMARY

The Great Lakes ecosystem is recognized by many as an international natural resource that has been altered by human activities and climate variability. These alterations have led to degraded water quality, diminished habitat, lower native fish and wildlife populations, and an altered ecosystem. In response, the federal governments of the United States and Canada and the state and provincial governments in the Great Lakes basin are implementing several restoration activities. These activities range from mitigating the harmful effects of toxic substances in lake waters to restoring fish habitat.

Most laws and efforts in the past addressed specific issues in the Great Lakes; a few addressed issues at the ecosystem level. This caused the Government Accountability Office and others to express the need for initiating and implementing a comprehensive approach for restoring the Great Lakes ecosystem. In 2010, the Great Lakes Restoration Initiative (GLRI) was proposed and implemented by the Obama Administration. The aim of GLRI is to restore the Great Lakes ecosystem under one initiative. Specifically, the GLRI is to restore and maintain the chemical,

---

[*] This is an edited, reformatted and augmented version of a Congressional Research Service publication, CRS Report for Congress R43249, from www.crs.gov, prepared for Members and Committees of Congress, dated September 30, 2013.

physical and biological integrity of the Great Lakes Basin Ecosystem by directing activities to address five focus areas: (1) toxic substances and Areas of Concern (these are areas in the Great Lakes that are environmentally degraded); (2) invasive species; (3) nearshore health and nonpoint source pollution; (4) habitat and wildlife protection and restoration; and (5) accountability, monitoring, evaluation, communication, and partnerships.

The Environmental Protection Agency (EPA) is the lead federal agency for implementing and administering GLRI. The EPA has received authority to distribute appropriated funds to several federal agencies, which then undertake restoration activities and projects. The EPA also administers grant programs to fund nonfederal projects and activities related to restoration. An interagency Great Lakes Task Force oversees the implementation of GLRI and created a strategy to guide restoration. The strategy (referred to as the Action Plan) provides a framework for restoring the Great Lakes ecosystem under GLRI from 2010 through 2014. For each focus area under the GLRI, the Action Plan provides a problem statement, a set of goals, interim objectives, progress measures, final targets, and principal activities for restoring the ecosystem. Restoration activities are being done under existing federal authorities. The GLRI has received approximately $1.37 billion in appropriated funds since FY2010.

The scope and scale of this restoration initiative have led some to question its direction and duration. The GLRI does not specify what a restored ecosystem might look like, nor does it estimate how long restoration activities will need to be conducted, and how much restoration might cost. Some other questions surrounding this initiative include how the GLRI is governed and how federal and state restoration efforts are coordinated. Furthermore, GLRI remains an administrative initiative; there is no law that specifically authorizes GLRI, though Congress has appropriated funds to implement the program. Congress might consider these questions in oversight hearings or in legislation during the 113th Congress. Companion bills have been introduced in the 113th Congress to address GLRI. S. 1232 and H.R. 2773 would establish an administrative and management structure for restoration activities in the Great Lakes, authorize GLRI and appropriations for its implementation, specify the scope and function of GLRI, and authorize the coordinating role of the Great Lakes Interagency Task Force.

INTRODUCTION

The Great Lakes ecosystem is the largest system of fresh surface water in the world. The watershed covers approximately 300,000 square miles and is shared by eight U.S. states (Illinois, Indiana, Michigan, Minnesota, New York, Ohio, Pennsylvania, and Wisconsin) and one Canadian province (Ontario). (See *Figure 1*.) The Great Lakes contain nearly 90% of the surface freshwater of the United States and 20% of the surface freshwater of the world. In the last several decades, agricultural activity throughout the basin, and urban and industrial development concentrated along the shoreline, have degraded water quality in the Great Lakes, posing potential threats to the ecosystem.

Source: U.S. Army Corps of Engineers, Detroit District.

Figure 1. The Great Lakes Basin.

Development has also led to changes in terrestrial and aquatic habitats, the introduction of nonnative species, the contamination of sediments, and the listing of more than 50 threatened or endangered species in the ecosystem.[1] In response to deteriorating conditions in the ecosystem, the federal governments of the United States and Canada and the state and provincial governments in the Great Lakes basin have implemented several restoration activities.[2]

An estimated 40 million people rely on the Great Lakes ecosystem for jobs, drinking water, and recreation, among other things. In economic terms, the present-value benefit in 2007 of restoring the Great Lakes was estimated to be $50 billion (in direct and indirect benefits) over the long term.[3] The ultimate cost for restoring the Great Lakes is unclear, but the value of the potential benefits of restoration has caused, in part, several in Congress to regard restoring the Great Lakes a priority. The U.S. Congress has played a role in restoration efforts in the Great Lakes and enacted more than 30 laws over several years focused on restoring aspects of the Great Lakes ecosystem. These laws have authorized activities ranging from mitigating the harmful effects of toxic substances on water quality to mitigating damages caused by invasive species. Most laws address specific issues in the Great Lakes; yet few address the entire ecosystem. Over the years, several stakeholders have expressed the need for initiating and implementing a comprehensive approach for restoring the Great Lakes ecosystem.[4]

Restoration efforts in the Great Lakes have been implemented over several decades by the federal government, states, and local stakeholders. Efforts have focused on specific aspects of the ecosystem, but rarely the entire ecosystem. For example, the Great Lakes Water Quality Agreement (GLWQA), initially signed in 1972 and then revised several times afterwards, addresses water quality characteristics in the Great Lakes, but not habitat issues.[5] After several years of restoration, the Government Accountability Office (GAO) concluded that progress in restoring the Great Lakes was slow and restoration efforts were too loosely organized.[6] Specific concerns included the slow rate of cleaning up toxic sediments, insufficient governance to provide direction for ecosystem restoration activities, and lack of a comprehensive plan to guide restoration of the Great Lakes ecosystem.[7]

In 2004 a federal Great Lakes Interagency Task Force (hereinafter referred to as the Task Force)[8] was created to provide strategic direction for Great Lakes policies on restoration and to form a regional collaboration of stakeholders interested in restoring the Great Lakes ecosystem. This collaboration was termed the Great Lakes Regional Collaboration. It consisted of over 1,500 stakeholders and released the Great Lakes Regional Collaboration Strategy (hereinafter referred to as the Strategy).[9] The Strategy recommended implementing a series of actions and activities to start the restoration of the Great Lakes ecosystem over a five-year period from 2006 to 2011. The Strategy encompassed eight issue areas: aquatic invasive species, fish and wildlife habitat (habitat/species), coastal health, contaminated sediments, nonpoint source pollution, toxic pollutants, indicators and information, and sustainable development. The total cost of implementing the Strategy was estimated to be $20 billion over the five-year period. The Strategy (as a whole) is not being implemented, although several restoration programs included in the Strategy are underway or ongoing in the Great Lakes Restoration Initiative (GLRI) and other federal and state activities.

GREAT LAKES RESTORATION INITIATIVE

The GLRI was proposed in 2009 by the Obama Administration, and implemented in 2010. The GLRI is derived from the Strategy and aims to be consistent with the Strategy and GLWQA. The goal of the GLRI is to restore and maintain the chemical, physical and biological integrity of the Great Lakes Basin Ecosystem by directing activities to address five focus areas:[10]

- toxic substances and Areas of Concern;[11]
- invasive species;
- nearshore health and nonpoint source pollution;
- habitat and wildlife protection and restoration;
- accountability, monitoring, evaluation, communication, and partnerships.

Federal efforts to restore the Great Lakes ecosystem are coordinated by the Task Force. The EPA, serving as chair of the Task Force, is the lead federal agency for implementing and administering the GLRI. In appropriations laws from FY2010 to FY2013, the EPA has been given authority to receive and distribute congressionally appropriated funds to several federal agencies, which then undertake restoration activities and projects in the Great Lakes. EPA also implements restoration activities that are funded by the GLRI through the Great Lakes National Program Office (GLNPO). Restoration activities are being done under existing federal authorities that address restoration in the Great Lakes. There is no single law that specifically authorizes the GLRI as a restoration initiative for the Great Lakes.

The implementation of the GLRI is being guided by recommendations from a Great Lakes Advisory Board (GLAB). The GLAB provides advice on Great Lakes protection and restoration policy, long term goals of protection and restoration, annual priorities to protect and restore the Great Lakes, and issues addressed by the Task Force.[12] GLAB consists of 18 members who represent nonfederal stakeholders (e.g., non-governmental organizations, state agencies, tribal interests, and universities, among others) in the GLRI. GLAB is also expected to provide advice on the implementation of the Great Lakes Water Quality Agreement.[13]

GLRI Action Plan

The implementation of GLRI is also being guided by a Great Lakes Restoration Initiative Action Plan (hereinafter referred to as the Action Plan), which was created by the Task Force.[14] The Action Plan provides a framework for restoring the Great Lakes ecosystem from 2010 through 2014.[15] The Action Plan was derived from the Strategy, as well as from several other area-specific plans and programs such as the GLWQA and Great Lakes Binational Toxic Strategy,[16] among others. For each focus area under the GLRI, the Action Plan provides a problem statement, a set of goals, interim objectives, progress measures, final targets, and principal activities for restoring the ecosystem. The principal actions in the Plan are not specific projects; rather, they are broad actions that address the objectives of the focus areas. Each year, federal agencies identify projects they plan to take to implement the Action Plan. Project selection is guided by criteria such as:

- ability to achieve measurable outcomes that are linked to high priority issues;
- ability to advance existing Great Lakes activities or the priorities of existing plans for restoring the Great Lakes, including, but not limited to, Lakewide Management Plans, Remedial Action Plans for Areas of Concern,[17] and the Great Lakes Binational Toxic Strategy;[18]
- feasibility of prompt implementation and ability to yield near-term tangible results;
- strong interagency or inter-organizational collaboration and coordination;
- adherence to the best available science;
- public support for the project; and
- low transaction costs and leverage of nonfederal resources.

Projects are geared toward meeting overall and interim goals under each focus area. Overall goals are thematic. For example, Goal 1 under Habitat and Wildlife Protection and Restoration Focus Area states that "protection and restoration of Great Lakes aquatic and terrestrial habitats, including physical, chemical, and biological processes and ecosystem functions, maintain or improve the conditions of native fish and wildlife." Interim goals have quantifiable measures such as "by 2014, 3,000 miles of Great Lakes rivers and tributaries will be reopened and 500 barriers to fish will be removed or bypassed." Measures of progress are quantifiable indicators that are related to the goals. For example, to evaluate progress in restoring habitat and wildlife protection, some measures used are miles of river reopened for fish passage, and percentage of U.S. coastal Great Lakes wetlands assessed. Measures have a quantified baseline and targets for each year between 2010 and 2014.

Monitoring and oversight mechanisms are also discussed in the Action Plan. An accountability system was created to measure and track progress of projects and the implementation of the Action Plan. Further, an interactive electronic map was created that shows the location and description of each project.[19]

Recipients of funding are required to submit status reports on projects and progress towards interim measures and goals of the Action Plan. The EPA collects these reports and compiles an annual report to the President on outcomes and measures.

The report also lists funding allocations for participating agencies by fiscal year. (See *Table 4.*) The most recent report discusses progress in FY2011. There are mixed results for meeting goals and targets, and in several cases, the report states that it is too early to evaluate progress and that several indicators cannot be determined.[20]

Funding

The estimated cost for implementing GLRI for the first five years is approximately $2.2 billion according to the Action Plan. There is no estimate as to how much it will take for the ecosystem to be fully restored, or how long the restoration effort is expected to take. It its inaugural year (FY2010), the GLRI received $475 million in appropriations provided to the EPA.[21] The EPA also was granted the authority to transfer funds to other federal agencies for restoration activities in the Great Lakes and provide grants to state, non-governmental, and private stakeholders. Of the funds appropriated, approximately $400 million were *new* funds that had not been associated with appropriations for existing federal restoration programs. Approximately $75 million was appropriated for existing EPA programs, which addressed Great Lakes restoration.

Funding for the next three years remained steady at approximately $300 million, and the Administration's request for FY2014 is $300 million.[22] (See *Table 1.*) In these appropriations laws, funds were given to the EPA to carry

out the GLRI as well as implement activities under the Great Lakes Water
Quality Agreement.

Restoration activities are funded through grants and transfers to other
federal agencies.

A transfer of funds to an agency is usually done through cooperative or
interagency agreements. Funds for other federal agencies are to be considered
new funds for restoration. Agencies are expected to maintain their base level
of funding for restoration activities and identify new activities to support
GLRI.

Therefore total annual funding for restoring the Great Lakes ecosystem is
funding for the GLRI plus funding for base restoration programs. Base funding
for Great Lakes ecosystem restoration activities has been reported in the Great
Lakes Ecosystem Restoration Crosscut Budget. For example, for FY2011,
base funding for Great Lakes restoration was approximately $677.0 million.
With GLRI funding, total funding for restoration was reported at $977.0
million.[23]

Table 1. Funding for GLRI, FY2010-FY2013 and FY2014 Administration's Request (in $millions)

Year	Funding
FY2010	$475.0
FY2011	$300.0
FY2012	$299.5
FY2013	$298.8[a]
FY2014 Request	$300.0

Source: Great Lakes Restoration Initiative at http://greatlakesrestoration.us/index.html
and Senate Committee on Appropriations, FY14 Interior Explanatory Statement,
at http://www.appropriations method=news.view&id=d103 7190-bf9c-420c-a8a5-
79c0ef9c495c.

[a] This figure reflects the 0.2% across the board rescission for FY2013, but not the
deductions due to sequestration. Figures are taken from Senate Committee on
Appropriations, FY14 Interior Explanatory Statement, at http://www.appro
priations.senate.gov/news.cfm?method=news.view&id=d1037190-bf9c-420c-
a8a5-79c0ef9c495c.

Implementation

GLRI has received appropriations from FY2010 to FY2013 and is being implemented according to the Action Plan. There has been over a billion dollars appropriated to implement GLRI via its five focus areas through FY2013. (See *Table 2.*) Most of the appropriations have gone to the EPA, with significant amounts of funding going to U.S. Fish and Wildlife Service (FWS), National Oceanic and Atmospheric Administration (NOAA), and the U.S. Army Corps of Engineers (Corps). Note that appropriations for EPA are for EPA directed programs and efforts, as well as grant programs for stakeholder research and restoration activities. (See *Table 3.*)

Table 2. Summary of Funding Allocation by Focus Area, FY2010-FY2013 and FY2014 Administration's Request (in $millions)

Focus Area	FY2010	FY2011	FY2012	FY2013	FY2014 request
Toxic Substances and Area of Concern	$146.9	$100.4	$106.3	n/a	$110.7
Invasive Species	60.3	57.5	57.5	n/a	53.0
Nearshore Health and Nonpoint Source Pollution	97.3	49.3	54.8	n/a	56.4
Habitat and Wildlife Protection and Restoration	105.3	63.0	56.8	n/a	58.8
Accountability, Education, Monitoring, Evaluation, Communication, and Partnerships	65.2	29.3	24.1	n/a	21.1
TOTAL	475.0	299.4	299.5	298.8	300.0

Source: U.S. Environmental Protection Agency, U.S. Environmental Protection Agency FY2014 Justification of Appropriation Estimates for the Committee on Appropriations, U.S. Environmental Protection Agency, Budget Justification, April 2013, pp. 284-285. n/a = not available.

Note: FY2013 funding for focus area categories has not been reported to include sequestration and the rescission in FY2013.

**Table 3. Allocation of GLRI Funds by Federal Agency, FY2010-FY2013
and FY2014 Administration's Request
(in $millions)**

Agency	FY2010	FY2011	FY2012	FY2013	FY2014 request
U.S. Coast Guard	$6.3	$2.7	$2.7	n/a	$1.9
National Oceanic and Atmospheric Administration	30.5	18.3	15.6	n/a	15.2
U.S. Army Corps of Engineers	49.6	31.4	33.8	n/a	20.6
Bureau of Indian Affairs	3.4	6.3	4.7	n/a	4.0
National Park Service	10.5	4.9	3.4	n/a	3.1
U.S. Fish and Wildlife Service	69.3	48.7	43.6	n/a	32.7
U.S. Geological Survey	23.7	14.5	12.4	n/a	11.4
Federal Highway Administration	2.5	1.2	1.2	n/a	1.0
Maritime Administration	4.0	2.7	2.4	n/a	2.3
Agency for Toxic Substances and Disease Registry	5.5	2.2	2.2	n/a	1.7
Animal and Plant Health Inspection Service	1.9	0.6	1.1	n/a	0.9
Natural Resources Conservation Service	34.1	16.8	24.2	n/a	23.3
U.S. Forest Service	15.5	8.9	6.7	n/a	6.3
Environmental Protection Agency (including International Joint Commission, Great Lakes Fisheries Commission, and other agreements)	218.1	140.1	145.5	n/a	156.1
Multiple Agencies: Asian Carp				n/a	19.5
TOTAL	475.0	299.4	299.5	298.824	300.0

Source: U.S. Environmental Protection Agency, U.S. Environmental Protection
Agency FY2014 Justification of Appropriation Estimates for the Committee on
Appropriations, U.S. Environmental Protection Agency, Budget Justification,
April 2013, pp. 284-285.

Note: FY2013 funding for agencies have not been reported to include sequestration
and the rescission in FY2013.

Implementation of GLRI is guided, in part, by provisions in the Interior and Related Agencies Appropriations laws and associated committee and conference reports. In FY2012 appropriations, for example, GLRI was instructed to follow guidelines under H.Rept. 112-151.[25] This committee report stated that EPA should transfer funds to other agencies more expeditiously. Further, the report states that funds are to supplement and expand existing programs, rather than supplant them. The committee report also directed EPA and other federal agencies to prioritize actions that implement "action-oriented" projects in lieu of additional studies, monitoring, and evaluations. Lastly, the report stated that the committee expects to see measurable results from funding over the last few years.[26]

ISSUES FOR CONGRESS

Since FY2010, the implementation of the GLRI represents a significant increase in funding and activities for Great Lakes restoration and a novel attempt at restoring the ecosystem holistically. Some issues with GLRI that have emerged include clarity about the management structure of GLRI, the potential integration of GLRI with existing federal and state restoration efforts in the Great Lakes, the effectiveness of the Action Plan in laying out a strategy for fully restoring the Great Lakes, the overall direction and duration of restoring the Great Lakes, and the funding needed to implement and complete the GLRI. Some of these issues are addressed, in part, by proposed legislation introduced in the 113th Congress. S. 1232 and H.R. 2773 would establish a governance and management structure for restoration activities in the Great Lakes, authorize GLRI and appropriations for its implementation, specify the scope and function of GLRI, and authorize the coordinating role of the Great Lakes Interagency Task Force. A summary of how these bills amend current law and analysis of how they might change current practices in GLRI is provided in the text box below. The rest of this section reviews the aforementioned issues that might be of interest to Congress.

Introduced Legislation Authorizing GLRI in 113th Congress

S. 1232 and H.R. 2773 are two bills in the 113th Congress that would amend the Federal Water Pollution Control Act (33 U.S.C. 1268 (a)) to authorize the GLRI and associated functions and activities related to its implementation.

The bills are largely similar, with some differences in the terms they would define, the structure of meetings held by GLAB, composition of the Task Force, and authorized funding for carry out projects that address remediation of sediment contamination in Areas of Concern. Broadly speaking, both bills would broaden the law to authorize the implementation of GLRI and related activities. Presently, the law authorizes the EPA to conduct restoration activities in the Great Lakes and coordinate activities with other federal agencies.

Both bills would update the findings and purpose of Section 118 to include attaining the goals detailed in the Great Lakes Restoration Initiative Action Plan (Action Plan), Great Lakes Regional Collaboration Strategy (Regional Strategy), and Great Lakes Water Quality Agreement (Agreement). In addition, both bills would expand the forms of federal collaboration in the Great Lakes region to include the funding of contracts and interagency agreements, as well as grants, for the protection, restoration, and pollution control in the ecosystem.

Both bills would amend the law to authorize the Great Lakes Advisory Board (GLAB), the Great Lakes Restoration Initiative (GLRI), and the Great Lakes Interagency Task Force (Task Force). The bills would specifically authorize GLRI to implement projects and activities that would implement the Strategy and Agreement. This would appear to broaden the scope of the GLRI as it would encompass several goals and objectives listed under the Strategy and Agreement. The bills state that federal agencies should maintain funding for baseline activities, and no funds would be provided for water infrastructure projects that also receive funding from state water pollution and drinking water revolving funds.

The Task Force under both bills would be the primary coordinating entity for restoration activities by collaborating with Canada, coordinating the development of federal restoration policies and projects, and assisting in the management of the Great Lakes System. The Task Force would also be responsible for developing outcome-based goals for the ecosystem, and reviewing and updating the Regional Strategy and Action Plan as necessary.

The Task Force would also provide reports to Congress that discusses what actions have been implemented or not implemented with recommendations for changes. The Administrator of the EPA would be responsible for submitting an annual progress report to Congress, and the Director of the Office of Management and Budget would be directed to submit a crosscut budget to Congress.

Both bills would authorize $475 million in appropriations for each of fiscal years 2014 to 2018 to implement GLRI. S. 1232 would authorize $150 million for each fiscal year from 2014 through 2018 for projects determined to address remediation of sediment contamination in areas of concern; H.R. 2773 only would authorize $100 million for each fiscal year from 2014 through 2018 for these projects. In addition, both S. 1232 and H.R. 2773 would authorize an additional $25 million for each fiscal year from 2014 through 2018 for the Great Lakes Program Office.

Implementation and Management of GLRI

Decision-Making

Restoration efforts in the Great Lakes have historically been conducted by several federal or state agencies, largely without a central organizing or governing entity. At the federal level, restoration activities have been conducted under various authorities, with several activities being implemented by the EPA through its Great Lakes National Program Office. In the past, the GAO suggested that a lack of centralized leadership in the Great Lakes restoration activities could detract from the effectiveness and prominence of restoration efforts.[27] Questions such as who is in charge, and how are the implementation of restoration activities to be governed, were posed.[28]

In part, GLRI has addressed these questions in program documents, but some questions about the governance of the restoration initiative remain. For example, it is unclear if a central governing structure that oversees all restoration activities (i.e., all federal, state, and local efforts) exists. The GLRI does not define a central governing structure or decision-making process for guiding all restoration efforts, but appears to promote EPA as the lead federal agency for implementing the initiative. For example, EPA received funds from FY2010 to FY2013 to implement the GLRI and was given authority to transfer these funds to other federal agencies to conduct GLRI activities. EPA was directed to provide annual reports that list funds given to each federal agency and describe program accomplishments. EPA created the Action Plan with the Great Lakes Task Force. While EPA appears to be in charge of implementing GLRI, it does not have the authority to direct the entire Great Lakes restoration effort that includes non-GLRI federal activities and activities done by non-federal stakeholders.[29] The Task Force appears to be responsible for coordinating all restoration activities in the Great Lakes ecosystem and for implementing the Action Plan an integrated manner.[30] These tasks, however, do not appear to constitute decision-making functions;[31] rather it promotes the Task Force as a coordinating entity for all restoration and resource management activities in the Great Lakes.

To temper this issue, the scope of GLRI might not be intended to cover all aspects of Great Lakes restoration. For example, the GLRI is focused on new federal activities and not pre-existing baseline activities, and does not include programs that address infrastructure that affects water quality. However, under this notion, it becomes apparent that GLRI should not be considered a centralized coordinating or management approach to restoring the Great Lakes. This might bring up the earlier question of whether lacking a centralized coordinating or management structure will negatively affect restoration in the Great Lakes.

Coordination

Lacking a coordinated effort to restore the Great Lakes ecosystem is an issue that has been raised in the past for Great Lakes restoration. The GAO asserted that restoration efforts in the Great Lakes suffered from inadequate coordination.[32] GLRI addresses this assertion by stating that it aims to build on existing federal, state, and local activities and draw upon a series of ongoing restoration efforts outlined in existing plans and programs.[33] Further, the Task Force is expected to coordinate Great Lakes restoration efforts among federal agencies.

It is unclear, however, how state and local restoration efforts in the Great Lakes are to be coordinated with the GLRI efforts. Coordination with nonfederal entities in the Great Lakes might be significant due to the number of entities involved in restoration, including efforts from eight states. Some might contend that absent a formal coordination role for nonfederal entities, restoration projects might overlap. Further, some contend that with greater coordination among federal and non-federal stakeholders, there might be opportunities to leverage federal resources with state or local resources to accomplish restoration projects.[34] There is no formal role for nonfederal representatives to coordinate with federal actions in a governance entity. The Task Force does not have nonfederal members. Coordination among nonfederal members could be addressed by the GLAB, however their charter does not specify that coordination is a priority. GLAB is to provide advice on the implementation of GLRI. Some have also questioned whether GLRI should have a formal collaboration with Canada and Ontario to coordinate restoration activities.

Some restoration activities conducted by nonfederal entities are done under the GLRI with grants from federal agencies. Grants are awarded for projects in one of the focus areas and grantees are required to input project information (description of work and project outputs) into the Great Lakes Accountability System (GLAS). This information could be used to facilitate coordinated approaches to restoration and to determine if projects have similar objectives, but non-GLRI projects are not inserted into GLAS making analysis of overlap or potential for collaboration difficult.

Outside of GLRI efforts there have been attempts to organize and report all federal and state activities related to ecosystem restoration in the Great Lakes. For example, in the last few years, the creation of a Great Lakes crosscut budget has been mandated by Congress in annual appropriations laws.[35] The resulting crosscut budget contained information on GLRI funding as well as other base federal funding for Great Lakes restoration. It also reported some state spending for restoration efforts; however, just Wisconsin reported funding for FY2012. Some might view the creation and dissemination of a broad crosscut budget as one tool to organize and potentially coordinate all Great Lakes restoration activities.

Examples from Other Restoration Initiatives

There are several approaches for addressing governance and coordination that are exemplified in other large-scale restoration initiatives that could be contemplated for the GLRI. For example, Congress could create a single entity that centrally coordinates restoration activities at all stakeholder levels. This could include all federal activities and state activities. The restoration initiative in the Platte River is guided by a Governance Committee (GC), which is responsible for implementing the Program.[36] The GC is a ten-member body with representatives from Colorado, Nebraska, and Wyoming, U.S. Bureau of Reclamation (USBR), U.S. Fish and Wildlife Service (FWS), water users, and environmental entities. The GC makes programmatic decisions including changes to budgets and changes to restoration activities. The GC justifies these types of changes with new information or recommendations from adaptive management efforts. An Oversight Committee, consisting of the Secretary of the Interior and the Governors of Colorado, Nebraska, and Wyoming, is responsible for approving significant modifications to the program.[37]

Several other ecosystem restoration initiatives are governed by hybrid entities with both federal and state partners. In some cases, these governing bodies are limited in their ability to make decisions. Their decision-making authority extends to certain types of decisions such as creating a restoration plan, conducting science, and monitoring restoration projects. However, project implementation might be left to individual state and federal agencies rather than the hybrid entity. Examples of this type of governing entity include the Chesapeake Bay Executive Council, Long Island Sound Study Policy Committee, and the South Florida Ecosystem Restoration Task Force.

S. 1232 and H.R. 2773

Bills in the 113th Congress address governance and coordination under GLRI. S. 1232 and H.R. 2773 would authorize the EPA to select programs and projects for Great Lakes protection and restoration. The bill states that the EPA would consult with federal partners, including the Task Force, and consider recommendations of GLAB, when selecting projects to implement.[38] The bill would also authorize the Task Force and direct it to carry out several coordinating activities related to restoring the Great Lakes ecosystem. Some examples include collaborating with Canada and bi-national bodies involved in activities related to the Great Lakes; managing the Great Lakes system, considering recommendations from GLAB; coordinating government actions associated with implementing restoration plans such as the Action Plan, Strategy, and GLWQA; and developing outcome-based goals for the Great Lakes System.[39] Under these bills, EPA would be the lead agency in implementing GLRI, and the Task Force would be the lead entity in coordinating overall federal and nonfederal efforts to address the Great Lakes ecosystem.

In addition, these bills would require the GLRI to prioritize work done by nonfederal partners for priority areas each year and would require that federal projects and nonfederal projects are implemented in coordination with states and other organizations.[40] Further, the bills would direct the Office of Management and Budget to create a Great Lakes crosscut budget to report funding and projects funded by GLRI and potentially other non-GLRI activities. The crosscut budget would also be required to identify all expenditures by federal and state governments on Great Lakes restoration activities since FY2004. If enacted, these bills would create a permanent requirement for creating a crosscut budget.

GLRI Action Plan

The lack of a comprehensive plan or strategy to guide restoration efforts in the Great Lakes was a concern in the past for restoration efforts in the Great

Lakes.[41] Without a plan, the GAO reported that organizations developed their own strategies for restoration, inadvertently making coordination among them difficult. The GLRI Action Plan was created in part to address this concern. The Action Plan discusses broad themes related to restoration and provides a set of short term goals for measuring progress. The Action Plan specifically states that it does not address water infrastructure programs that include the Clean Water or Drinking Water State Revolving Fund program, nor base federal agency restoration activities. Some could contend that the Action Plan still is not a comprehensive plan for restoration because some restoration themes and projects are not included. For example, the Action Plan lists themes that are to be addressed by restoration activities, but does not provide details on specific restoration projects that are to be implemented or how projects are connected to the restoration of the ecosystem. Further, the Action Plan does not cover all federal restoration activities (e.g., those ongoing restoration activities initiated before GLRI and the Action Plan were created) and does not include or address all state or local restoration activities.

To counter these points some might contend that the scope of the Action Plan is only based on implementing GLRI (i.e., not all federal restoration activities) and that specificity of projects to be funded and implemented depends on annual decisions and recommendations made by the EPA, participating federal agencies, and the Task Force. Therefore, it would not be possible to list all restoration projects upfront. Further, they might contend that broad restoration actions in the Great Lakes ecosystems are also, in part, guided by the Strategy and the Great Lakes Water Quality Agreement. The Strategy lists thematic areas for restoration and key actions for restoration; and GLWQA contains long term goals for restoration that would encompass all restoration activities related to water quality. Both bills in the 113th Congress would authorize restoration actions to achieve goals established in the Action Plan, Strategy, and GLWQA.[42] This would create a broader restoration effort that goes beyond just implementing the Action Plan and would include actions and goals in both the Strategy and GLWQA.

Examples of Non-GLRI Activities Related to Restoration

There are several restoration activities in the Great Lakes that are not covered under GLRI. These activities are termed base-level restoration activities, and are generally restoration activities that federal agencies have been implementing in the Great Lakes ecosystem before GLRI was initiated.

The exception to this description is some base activities implemented by the EPA that directly address the Great Lakes (e.g., remediation of contaminated sediments in the Great Lakes ecosystem), which are included in GLRI. Further, several of the base-level activities are implemented on a national level with a national level scope and purpose. A portion of program funds are invested in the Great Lakes region and these activities generally have secondary benefits for restoring the Great Lakes ecosystem. The appropriations estimated for non-GLRI restoration activities are much higher than GLRI appropriations. For example, in FY2012, non-GLRI restoration activities were appropriated approximately $579 million (GLRI was appropriated $300 million). Of this amount, nearly 87% was for national level programs.

Some selected examples of non-GLRI restoration activities include:

- Agricultural conservation programs administered by the Natural Resources Conservation Service such as the Environmental Quality Incentives Program and the Wetlands Reserve Program
- Clean Water State Revolving Fund administered by the EPA
- Coastal Zone Management grants administered by the National Oceanic and Atmospheric Administration
- National Wildlife Refuge System (in the Great Lakes region) and Great Lakes Fish and Wildlife Restoration program administered by FWS
- Great Lakes Fishery Commission overseen by the U.S. Department of State

Issues related to the implementation of the Action Plan could raise questions about how the Action Plan will integrate GLRI activities with existing federal, state, and local activities. The GLRI does not include all federal and nonfederal actions related to restoring the Great Lakes in the Action Plan.[43] It specifically states that it will guide the implementation of the GLRI, not necessarily all restoration efforts in the Great Lakes ecosystem.[44] The Action Plan does state that it will build upon past programs and plans that are now in place. It is unclear if the project selection, oversight, and reporting requirements under GLRI directly cover non-GLRI activities in addition to taking them into consideration.

If GLRI does not cover all new and existing federal activities, some questions might arise, including:

- Will GLRI reporting and oversight activities include non-GLRI funded efforts?
- How will GLRI integrate non-GLRI projects in the restoration effort, or how would duplication of efforts be avoided?
- Are interim goals and overall goals a true indication of GRLI efforts?
- Will federal agencies maintain non-GLRI activities or eventually integrate them into GLRI?

Some of these questions might be addressed in the pending revision to the Action Plan which addresses restoration activities from 2015 to 2019. Some contend that the revised Action Plan should contain greater emphasis on monitoring and adaptive management and focus on achieving and assessing outcome-oriented results (i.e., results that reflect the condition of the ecosystem) rather than just output-oriented results (i.e., results that are reported from specific projects).[45] Creating a revised Action Plan based on the results and outcomes of projects implemented under the first Action Plan could be difficult if sufficient results have not been reported in time for the revision. This might not allow for the revised Action Plan to incorporate lessons learned and project results from the first phase of restoration.

Vision of a Restored Great Lakes Ecosystem

The GLRI does not present an overall vision for what a restored Great Lakes ecosystem should look like and function. An overall vision is broadly discussed in the Action Plan,[46] but specific goals and targets for restoration are provided for just the first four years of restoration. Furthermore, there is no indication of how long it will take to restore the Great Lakes ecosystem. The Task Force, under GLAB, is currently revising the Action Plan to describe activities and goals from FY2015 to FY2019, yet it is unclear if this represents a stage for restoration or a plan to complete restoration. Some might counter this concern by noting that it is difficult to fully contemplate a restored Great Lakes ecosystem because of its size and complexity. They might also point to the Great Lakes Water Quality Agreement as a guiding document for long-term restoration. The Agreement contains general objectives for restoring the waters of the Great Lakes, including that the waters should be a source of high-quality drinking water, free from pollutants that could be harmful to humans, and support healthy and productive wetlands, among other things.[47] Further, the Agreement contains 10 Annexes that describe long-term objectives for addressing specific issues related to restoration such as diminishing excess nutrient deposition (e.g., phosphorus and nitrogen) and controlling aquatic invasive species, among others. In the GLWQA there is no indication of how long it will take to restore the waters of the Great Lakes, nor estimate of how much it will cost.

The lack of defining what a restored ecosystem might resemble under the GLRI or how long it might take restore the ecosystem could generate questions related to how much restoring and maintaining the Great Lakes ecosystem could ultimately cost. Other questions might include what the long-terms plans are for restoration and if any major restoration projects are being contemplated; and if restoration might involve manipulating water flows into or out of the Great Lakes to enhance habitat for native species or restrict the entry of aquatic nuisance species. Answers to these questions could involve actions that could be potentially controversial. [48]

Long-term issues associated with the Great Lakes ecosystem such as the control and eradication of invasive species or the potential effects of climate change might not be adequately addressed in five-year increments. This and other restoration issues might require a longer planning horizon than five years to address. The potential effects of climate change on the Great Lakes ecosystem should be incorporated into the Action Plan according to some.[49] The Action Plan addresses climate change by noting that it could have implications for focus areas and would be addressed where appropriate. Some contend that addressing the effects of climate change in the selection and implementation of restoration projects is important for the long term viability of restoration.[50] Climate change could potentially alter Great Lakes water levels, which have a significant connection to several ecosystem properties and economic factors in the Great Lakes.

S. 1232 and H.R. 2773 address this issue, in part, by authorizing the Task Force to review the Strategy and Action Plan every five years. The Task Force would be authorized to update and revise the Action Plan. This policy would allow for revisions to reflect changes in the ecosystem, but might not generate a vision for the restored ecosystem or result in providing the estimated duration of restoration.

Progress of Restoring the Great Lakes under the GLRI

Implementation of GLRI began in 2010; however, it is unclear how much more is needed to restore the ecosystem. GLRI aims to track progress of restoration within the timeframe of the Action Plan. GLRI has an accountability system (Great Lakes Accountability System; GLAS) that lists projects and provides a description and their funding.[51] Further, GLAS requests project managers to identify the focus area they are working under and any quantifiable results from the project (e.g., acres of wetlands restored). GLAS documentation does suggest that results from projects could be aggregated and tracked, and that information will allow managers to adjust priorities based on data derived from GLAS. However, based on this description, some might contend that it is unclear how the completion or progress of these projects relates to the overall restoration of the ecosystem or ecosystem processes. For example, one researcher commented that many of the restoration projects are completed in "silos" without a comprehensive assessment of how projects relate to overall restoration.[52] In addition, he questioned whether measuring and reporting indicators will provide an understanding of how the overall ecosystem is improving or increasing its resilience. Others emphasize that outcomes of the restoration initiative are unclear, even though indicators and measurements are reported. In response to these claims, GLRI notes that monitoring and evaluation of progress is conducted on a regular basis.[53] Further, GLAS is expected to release a set of "dashboard indicators" that aim to provide a visual representation of progress toward metrics.[54] To address this point, some have called for broadening monitoring, and reframing the analyses and reporting of the results so that progress toward outcomes can be evaluated.[55] Both proposed bills authorizing GLRI in the 113th Congress would direct the Task Force to create outcome based goals for the Great Lakes. This could address, in part, the issue of evaluating restoration progress at the regional or ecosystem level, rather than at the project level. However, developing outcome based goals could be perceived as different from developing a strategy for achieving outcomes.

The GLRI accountability approach under GLAS appears only to be applicable to GLRI projects. It is unclear if it will be expanded to include non-GLRI and nonfederal activities. Without taking into account all efforts to restore the ecosystem, it would be difficult to evaluate the effectiveness and progress of GLRI. If GLRI and non-GLRI activities are contributing to restoration, how does one evaluate only GLRI activities? Progress toward meeting goals was reported in annual reports to Congress for FY2010 and FY2011. Progress reported for GLRI is mixed in these reports with several entries stating that indicators have not yet been determined. The reports also do not differentiate between progress made by GLRI projects versus non-GLRI federal and state actions. To counter this sentiment, one could contend that progress toward goals may not be measurable after a few years of implementing restoration activities. For many ecological indicators, progress might not be seen until several years after restoration actions have been implemented.

There do not appear to be any consequences for not progressing or reaching goals set by the GLRI. For example, if restoration targets are not being met, there does not appear to be a policy mechanism to alter the implementation or direction of GLRI efforts. Several other restoration initiatives have had mixed experiences working with quantitative goals and indicators of progress. For example, in the Chesapeake Bay and the Everglades restoration initiatives, some initial goals have not been met on schedule, resulting in criticism of the initiative. Policy mechanisms to address these shortcomings include revising the goals and indicators of progress, or implementing an adaptive management program.[56] Adaptive management can also be a policy tool that would allow changes in projects and goals if new circumstances arise or if progress stalls. The GLRI encourages agencies to incorporate adaptive management in implementing restoration projects, but has not implemented an adaptive management process. A recent draft report, however, proposes an adaptive management framework for restoration activities in the Great Lakes.[57] The objective of this framework would be to address programmatic decisions related to restoration. It would also address priorities for implementing projects and refine decision-making. Adaptive management can also be implemented on the programmatic scale. It could be used to measure and potentially adjust how the program is being implemented and how overall restoration objectives are being met.[58]

The lack of long-term restoration targets and a vision for a restored ecosystem might make measuring the progress of restoration difficult. Indeed, some have noted that GLRI projects and their outputs should be connected to an over-arching plan for restoration.[59] GLRI has a set of defined targets that are intended to be a measure of progress for restoring the Great Lakes. The targets are quantifiable and are listed for each year between 2010 and 2014 under each focus area.[60] However, restoration targets beyond the five-year frame are not discussed in the Action Plan.[61] This brings up the question of how many goals or steps are needed to be met for fully restoring the Great Lakes, and where is the current Great Lakes ecosystem on this scale. Several other large-scale ecosystem restoration initiatives have estimated the total duration and cost for restoration, yet most of them have had to alter their funding and time of completion estimates as restoration progressed.

Value of Restoring the Great Lakes

The question of whether an ecosystem restoration initiative is worth funding and whether restoration will ultimately provide an overall net financial benefit to the region has been brought up for several ecosystem restoration initiatives, including the Great Lakes. Answering this question for the Great Lakes is complicated since the total cost of restoration and its duration is unclear. The Brookings Institution has asserted that restoring the Great Lakes will not only help the ecosystem, but will provide an economic benefit to the region.[62] Their 2007 study reported the estimated financial benefits associated with improvements in Great Lakes environmental quality included higher catch rates in recreational fisheries, lower water treatment costs, more and better swimming opportunities, improved bird watching, more hunting opportunities, and benefits from removal of contaminated sediment. The sum of present-value benefits in 2007 from specific improvements in the environment totaled approximately $50 billion for long-term gains and $30-$50 billion for short-term gains.[63] The full cost of restoration, however, was not identified in this study making it impossible to evaluate the net benefit of restoration.

The total cost of funding the complete restoration of the Great Lakes ecosystem has not been estimated by the GLRI. GLRI estimates that $2.2 billion in funding is needed for the first five years of the restoration. It is unknown how much funding it will take to restore the ecosystem and what the ultimate benefits of restoration might be.[64] Further, it is unclear where along the restoration timeline GLRI might be because the problem and proposed solution has not been fully defined. Reporting by GLRI does not project how much longer restoration might take. Whether the first phase (2010 through 2014) covers a small or large space along the restoration timeline might influence decisions on how much funding to provide for the initiative.

Questions related to the cost of restoring the Great Lakes ecosystem and whether that cost is justified could be heightened because annual funding for restoring the Great Lakes is larger than that for other prominent ecosystems. Funding for all federal restoration activities in the Great Lakes has ranged from $649 million to $687 million annually from FY2004 to FY2009.[65] With GLRI, the FY2010 federal funding for Great Lakes restoration was approximately $1.2 billion (non-GLRI funding was approximately $720 million). Other ecosystem restoration efforts in areas such as the Everglades and Chesapeake Bay have lower annual federal funding (e.g., approximately $350 million and $400 - $450 million annually, respectively). Some might contend that the expansive size of the Great Lakes ecosystem warrants a higher price tag than other large-scale ecosystem restoration initiatives in the United States, and that funding needs for restoration are on par with other ecosystems. Further, they might argue that the Great Lakes ecosystem is one of the largest in the country, and potentially could contribute the greatest value to people. However, some others might contend that federal funding for GLRI is too high because combined with non-GLRI funding it is higher than any other ecosystem.

S. 1232 would authorize $475 million for each fiscal year from FY2014 to FY2018 to carry out GLRI. Further, it would authorize $150 million for each fiscal year during the same period to carry out projects that address remediation of sediment contamination in Areas of Concern, and $25 million for each fiscal year during the same period for the Great Lakes Program Office to administer and conduct restoration activities. H.R. 2773 would authorize the same amount of funding for GLRI and the Program Office, and $100 million for addressing remediation of sediment contamination in Areas of Concern.

CONCLUSION

The GLRI is a large-scale ecosystem restoration initiative that aims to restore the Great Lakes ecosystem under the framework of an Action Plan. It attempts to address past criticisms of Great Lakes restoration activities that included claims of a loosely coordinated restoration effort, and a restoration effort that lacks a comprehensive plan. The Great Lakes ecosystem is complex and covers a vast geographical area. This inherently leads to scientific uncertainties in implementing restoration projects and unforeseen circumstances in the evolution of the ecosystem. These factors and others may cause restoration efforts under the GLRI to face persistent and new questions by Congress and other stakeholders. Some might question how long restoration in the Great Lakes may take and how much it could ultimately cost. Further, questions related to how the GLRI is implemented and whether it will eventually encompass all federal activities, state activities, and local activities related to Great Lakes restoration could be asked and discussed. The GLRI is not authorized in law, but in the 113th Congress, two bills were introduced to authorize the initiative. Both bills would address similar issues, including authorizing the EPA as the lead agency for implementing GLRI, and authorizing the Task Force to coordinate among federal and non-federal stakeholders. They would also authorize $475 million annually from FY2014 to FY2018 to fund GLRI activities.

End Notes

[1] These are species listed under the U.S. Endangered Species Act (16 U.S.C. §§1531-1544). For a more detailed summary of causes and symptoms of ecosystem deterioration in the Great Lakes, see Donald Scavia et al., Prescription for Great Lakes Ecosystem Protection and Restoration, National Wildlife Federation, Report, December 2005, pp. 1- 39.

[2] For more information on U.S. federal and state programs aimed at restoring the Great Lakes, see U.S. Government Accountability Office, Great Lakes: An Overall Strategy and Indicators for Measuring Progress Are Needed to Better Achieve Restoration Goals, GAO-03-515 (Washington, DC: April 2003). Hereafter referred to as An Overall Strategy and Indicators for Measuring Progress Are Needed to Better Achieve Restoration Goals.

[3] John C. Austin et al., Healthy Waters, Strong Economy: The Economic Benefits of Restoring the Great Lakes Ecosystem, The Brookings Institution, September 2007.

[4] For example, see An Overall Strategy and Indicators for Measuring Progress Are Needed to Better Achieve Restoration Goals, and Melissa Malott, Restoration Plan Key to Helping Lake Michigan, Other Great Lakes, Clean Wisconsin, May 29, 2008.

[5] The Agreement addresses shared priorities of the United States and Canada with respect to the Great Lakes and aims to restore and protect the chemical, physical, and biological integrity of the waters of the Great Lakes.

[6] See An Overall Strategy and Indicators for Measuring Progress Are Needed to Better Achieve Restoration Goals.

[7] Ibid.

[8] The Great Lakes Interagency Task Force was created by an executive order in 2002 (E. O. 12240). Its purpose is to provide strategic direction on federal Great Lakes policy. The Task Force is chaired by the Administrator of the U.S. Environmental Protection Agency (EPA) and contains 10 agency and cabinet-level officers.

[9] The Great Lakes Regional Collaboration Strategy can be found at http://www.glrc.us/strategy.html.

[10] GLRI does not include water supply issues, which are addressed through the Great Lakes-St. Lawrence River Basin Water Resources Compact. Water infrastructure needs in the Great Lakes are not addressed by the GLRI, but through funding provided by the Drinking Water State Revolving Loans and the Clean Water State Revolving Funds in EPA.

[11] Areas of Concern are geographic areas within the Great Lakes Basin that have been designated for restoration under Annex 2 of the Great Lakes Water Quality Agreement. Specifically, these areas " fail to meet the general or specific objectives of the Agreement where such failure has caused or is likely to cause impairment of beneficial use of the area's ability to support aquatic life."

[12] U.S. Environmental Protection Agency Charter, Great Lakes Advisory Board, Filed June 22, 2012, http://www.epa.gov/ocem/faca/pdf/2012/2012_glab_charter_establishment.pdf.

[13] Ibid, section 3.

[14] White House Council on Environmental Quality, U.S. Environmental Protection Agency, et al., Great Lakes Restoration Initiative Action Plan, Great Lakes Interagency Task Force, February 21, 2010. Hereafter referred to as The GLRI Action Plan.

[15] The Task Force is planning to revise the Action Plan for FY2015 to FY2019.

[16] The Great Lakes Binational Toxic Strategy is a strategy put forth by Canada and the United States that aims to virtually eliminate persistent toxic substances resulting from human activities in the Great Lakes Basin. See the Strategy at http://binational.net/bns/strategy_en.pdf

[17] In 1987, the United States and Canada identified 43 Areas of Concern (AOC) in the Great Lakes basin that represented the most degraded portions of the ecosystem. The most common reason for degradation in AOCs is contaminated sediments.

[18] For a full list of pre-existing plans, see page 11 of The GLRI Action Plan.

[19] See http://greatlakesrestoration.us/

[20] U.S. Environmental Protection Agency and Great Lakes Interagency Task Force, Great Lakes Restoration Initiative: Fiscal Year. 2011 Report to Congress and the President, U.S. Environmental Protection Agency, September 2011, pp. 1-44, http://greatlakesrestoration.us/pdfs/2011-glri-report-to-congress.pdf.

[21] P.L. 111-88.

[22] FY2013 funding numbers are not necessarily comparable to other years because post-sequestration funding estimates are not publically available.

[23] Office of Management and Budget, Great Lakes Crosscut Report to Congress, Office of Management and Budget, May 2011, pp. 38.

[24] Figures are taken from Senate Committee on Appropriations, FY14 Interior Explanatory Statement, at http://www.appropriations.senate.gov/news.cfm?method=news.view&id=d1037190-bf9c-420c-a8a5-79c0ef9c495c.

[25] U.S. Congress, House Committee on Appropriations, Department of Interior, Environment, and Related Agencies Appropriations Bill, 2012, Report to Accompany H.R. 2584, 112th Cong., 1st sess., July 19, 2011, H.Rept. 112-151 (Washington: GPO, 2011), pp. 64-65.

[26] U.S. Congress, House Committee on Appropriations, Department of Interior, Environment, and Related Agencies Appropriations Bill, 2012, Report to Accompany H.R. 2584, 112th Cong., 1st sess., July 19, 2011, H.Rept. 112-151 (Washington: GPO, 2011), pp. 64-65.

[27] U.S. Government Accountability Office, Organizational Leadership and Restoration Goals Need to Be Better Defined for Monitoring Restoration Progress, Highlights of GAO-04-1024, September 2004, p. 1.

[28] Ibid.

[29] Non-federal stakeholders are expected to receive funding from GLRI through grants. They are also expected to work with EPA to establish a process to provide guidance for implementing the GLRI. Further, one longterm goal of the draft Action Plan is to create mechanisms that give stakeholders and citizens the opportunity to provide input to governments on Great Lakes issues and concerns.

[30] GLRI Action Plan, p. 13.

[31] Decision-making actions could include actions such as directing which projects to implement; directing the implementation of the restoration initiative, including making changes to implementation; defining the scope of restoration; and allocating funds.

[32] An Overall Strategy and Indicators for Measuring Progress Are Needed to Better Achieve Restoration Goals, p. 35.

[33] GLRI Action Plan, p. 11.

[34] For example, see Lynn McClure, Joel Brammeier, and John Jackson, Comments on the Great Lakes Restoration Initiative Action Plan Update, Healing Our Waters-Great Lakes Coalition, July 12, 2013, p. 7. Hereafter referred to as Comments on the GLRI Action Plan Update.

[35] For example, see P.L. 112-74, section 737.

[36] For more information, see https://www.platteriverprogram.org/AboutPRRIP/Pages/Program Information.aspx.

[37] The modifications are specified in the Final Platte River Recovery Implementation Program, and include such factors as changing the regulatory certainty afforded under the Program.

[38] Section 2(b)(4) of S. 1232.

[39] Section 2(b)(5) of S. 1232.

[40] Section 2(b)(4) of S. 1232.

[41] An Overall Strategy and Indicators for Measuring Progress Are Needed to Better Achieve Restoration Goals, p. 35.

[42] See section 2(a)(2) of S. 1232.

[43] The GLRI Action Plan, p. 13.

[44] The Action Plan notes that it is not the "only tool in the toolbox" referring to other programs that address restoration. See The GLRI Action Plan, p. 4.

[45] For example, see Comments on the GLRI Action Plan Update, p. 2.

[46] The GLRI Action Plan, p. 9.

[47] Article 3(1)(a) of the Great Lakes Water Quality Agreement.

[48] This issue has generated controversy among stakeholders bordering Lake Ontario. A proposal by the International Joint Commission to alter water flows from the Moses Saunders Dam and other structures for ecosystem restoration and other purposes have caused some property owners along the southern shore of Lake Ontario to criticize the plan because of its potential to flood their property.

[49] Comments on the GLRI Action Plan Update, p. 3.

[50] Comments on the GLRI Action Plan Update, p. 3.

[51] U.S. Environmental Protection Agency, Great Lakes Restoration Initiative Accountability System User Guide, Version 1.11, March 2012, p. 1, http://www.glri.us/granteeinfo.html.

[52] Don Scavia, "Avoiding the Tipping Point: A Decade of Developments," Session Talk, Milwaukee, WI, September 10, 2013.

[53] Cameron Davis, "Avoiding the Tipping Point: A Decade of Developments," Response to Session Talk, Milwaukee, WI, September 10, 2013.

[54] U.S. Environmental Protection Agency, Great Lakes Restoration Initiative Accountability System User Guide, Version 1.11, March 2012, p. 1, http://www.glri.us/granteeinfo.html.

[55] Don Scavia, "Avoiding the Tipping Point: A Decade of Developments," Session Talk, Milwaukee, WI, September 10, 2013.

[56] Adaptive management is the process of incorporating new scientific and programmatic information into the implementation of a project or plan to ensure that the goals of the activity are being reached efficiently. It promotes flexible decision-making to modify existing activities or create new activities if new circumstances arise (e.g., new scientific information) or if projects are not meeting their goals.

[57] Science Subgroup of the Great Lakes Regional Working Group, Great Lakes Restoration Initiative: Adaptive Science-Based Framework for Great Lakes Restoration, Great Lakes Regional Working Group, Draft Report, May 21, 2013, pp. 1-32.

[58] For more information on adaptive management, see CRS Report R41671, Adaptive Management for Ecosystem Restoration: Analysis and Issues for Congress, coordinated by Charles V. Stern.

[59] Comments on the GLRI Action Plan Update, p. 7.

[60] These measures of progress are listed in the Action Plan.

[61] The Great Lakes Water Quality Agreement, however, has some long-term restoration targets and objectives that do not appear to be time-limited.

[62] John C. Austin et al., Healthy Waters, Strong Economy: The Economic Benefits of Restoring the Great Lakes Ecosystem, The Brookings Institution, September 2007.

[63] John C. Austin et al., Healthy Waters, Strong Economy: The Economic Benefits of Restoring the Great Lakes Ecosystem, The Brookings Institution, September 2007.

[64] For comparison, the Great Lakes Regional Collaboration Strategy calls for spending $20 billion over a five-year period to restore the Great Lakes ecosystem. Of this total, $13.7 billion in new funds is for wastewater treatment system improvements (the anticipated federal share is $7.5 billion and nonfederal share is $6.2 billion), and $1.3 billion for improvement of drinking water treatment facilities. These activities are specifically not included in the Action Plan. See The Great Lakes Regional Collaboration, The Great Lakes Regional Collaboration Strategy (December 2005), accessed at http://www.glrc.us/.

[65] Office of Management and Budget, Great Lakes Restoration Crosscut: Report to Congress, Office of Management and Budget, Washington, DC, March 2010, http://www.whitehouse.gov/sites/default/files/omb/assets/ legislative_reports/2010_great_lakes_report.pdf.

In: Ecosystem Restoration
Editor: Simon Acheson

ISBN: 978-1-63117-540-4
© 2014 Nova Science Publishers, Inc.

Chapter 4

EVERGLADES RESTORATION: FEDERAL FUNDING AND IMPLEMENTATION PROGRESS[*]

Charles V. Stern

SUMMARY

The Everglades is a unique network of subtropical wetlands in South Florida that is approximately half of its historical size, due in part to degradation from federal water projects. In 2000, Congress authorized a 30-year plan, termed the Comprehensive Everglades Restoration Plan (CERP), for the restoration of the Everglades ecosystem in southern Florida. When originally authorized, it was estimated that CERP would cost a total of $8.2 billion and take approximately 30 years to complete. More recent estimates indicate that the plan would take approximately 50 years to implement, and would cost $13.5 billion.

Under CERP, the federal government (through the U.S. Army Corps of Engineers and the Department of the Interior) is required to fund half of the costs for restoration, with an array of state, tribal, and local agencies paying the other half. In addition to activities under CERP, a number of other federal and state efforts that pre-date CERP (known collectively as "non-CERP," or "Foundation" activities) also contribute to

---

[*] This is an edited, reformatted and augmented version of a Congressional Research Service publication, CRS Report for Congress R42007, from www.crs.gov, prepared for Members and Committees of Congress, dated July 30, 2013.

Everglades restoration. While non-CERP efforts are technically not included in CERP, the two sets of activities are widely viewed as complementary.

Since passage of CERP in 2000, the federal investment in the Everglades has increased. As of the end of FY2012, the federal government had provided about $1 billion in funding for CERP, with the state providing matching funds for CERP projects, as well as advanced funding for land acquisition and construction for expected future CERP projects. Federal funding for non-CERP activities (most of which pre-date CERP) has also continued over this time period. These efforts are estimated to total more than $3 billion as of 2012. While estimates of nonfederal (i.e., state) funding contributions to CERP and related restoration efforts vary widely depending on what methodology and assumptions are used, most agree that to date, the state of Florida has spent significantly more on Everglades restoration than has the federal government.

Progress has been made on a number of Everglades restoration projects, although overall progress to date has fallen short of initial goals. As of 2013, the majority of the land necessary for restoration projects under CERP had been acquired, and significant progress has been made on non-CERP activities (including improved water deliveries to Everglades National Park). Construction has also been initiated on four CERP projects, and studies have been completed or are underway for a number of other CERP projects. Despite this progress, some projects have seen setbacks in the form of schedule delays and cost escalations. Additionally, new or revised authorizations will be required for many projects to go forward. These impediments may have the effect of further delaying restoration efforts.

Reductions to state funding and the status of potential new CERP project authorizations under in the proposed Water Resources Development Act (S. 601) have increased attention to the congressional role in facilitating Everglades restoration during the 113th Congress. Debate and resolution of these issues has implications, both for ecosystem restoration in the Everglades and for large-scale restoration initiatives elsewhere.

This report provides information on federal funding for Everglades restoration. It also provides a brief overview of some of the accomplishments and potential challenges for Everglades restoration.

INTRODUCTION

The Florida Everglades is a unique network of subtropical wetlands that is now half its historical size. The federal government has had a long history of involvement in the Everglades, beginning in the 1940s with the U.S. Army Corps of Engineers (hereinafter referred to as the Corps) constructing flood control projects that shunted water away from the Everglades to make way for agricultural and urban development. Additional factors, including nonfederal development efforts, have contributed to the shrinking and altering of the Everglades ecosystem.

In recognition of the unique ecosystem services provided by the Everglades, federal and state agencies began ecosystem restoration activities in the Everglades in the early 1990s. However, it was not until 2000 that federal and state restoration activities were coordinated under an integrated plan. In the Water Resources Development Act of 2000 (WRDA 2000, P.L. 106-541), Congress approved the Comprehensive Everglades Restoration Plan (CERP) as a framework for Everglades restoration and authorized an initial round of projects by the Corps and the Department of the Interior (DOI). According to the process, additional Everglades projects are to be presented to Congress for authorization as their planning is completed. In WRDA 2007 (P.L. 110-114), four additional projects were authorized. As of early 2013, four other projects had feasibility studies completed but were not yet authorized.

To date, some progress has been made on Everglades restoration, but much more time and funding will be required to complete restoration as currently contemplated. Previously some have highlighted the overall slow pace of restoration as an argument for expedited support. Conversely, others have argued that restoration activities in the Everglades already receive too much funding relative to other priorities, and that the support provided for these activities is not appropriate given larger fiscal concerns.

Stakeholders involved with planning other large-scale restoration initiatives look to the Everglades as a model and a test case. Some believe the types of activities funded and the level of funding for the Everglades may set a precedent for other restoration initiatives, and should thus be a priority. Others assert that Everglades restoration efforts have been disproportionately favored relative to similar projects, and should be subject to the same cost-cutting efforts as other areas of the budget.

This report summarizes historical and current funding trends for Everglades restoration, with a focus on federal funding and recent issues facing Congress. It also provides a brief summary of some of the major accomplishments in Everglades restoration since the enactment of CERP in 2000, as well as ongoing challenges.

EVERGLADES PROJECTS: CERP AND NON-CERP

Federal CERP funding was first authorized in WRDA 2000, with a focus on increasing storage of excess water in the rainy season to provide more water during the dry season for the ecosystem and for urban and agricultural users. It is estimated that CERP will take more than 50 years and $13.5 billion to complete.[1] The federal government is expected to pay half of CERP's costs, and an array of state, tribal, and local agencies (i.e., nonfederal sponsors) will pay the other half. This same cost share is expected to apply to all project operation and maintenance costs.

WRDA 2000 authorized initial projects, established federal/nonfederal cost-sharing ratios for Everglades restoration, and created a process for additional projects to be authorized as part of the CERP framework. WRDA 2007 authorized an additional three CERP projects. Four other projects have completed the study phase and are ready for construction authorization. The status of these projects is discussed later in this report.

Federal Everglades restoration activities not authorized under CERP are often referred to as "nonCERP" or "Foundation" activities. Depending on how broadly this category is defined, it can encompass a wide variety of Everglades restoration activities undertaken by multiple agencies.[2] Most (but not all) of the authorities for this funding predate the enactment of CERP in 2000. However, similar to CERP funding, most funding for non-CERP Everglades restoration is provided to the Department of the Interior and the Corps of Engineers. Thus, the Corps and DOI are often the focal point for funding debates surrounding the Everglades.

FUNDING FOR EVERGLADES RESTORATION

Federal funding for Everglades restoration is largely provided through DOI and the Corps, and is concentrated in two appropriations bills—the Interior and Environment appropriations bill (which provides funds to DOI) and the Energy and Water Development appropriations bill (which provides funds to the Corps). Additionally, some funding in other appropriations bills is sometimes noted as contributing to Everglades restoration, but is not formally tracked under the Administration's non-CERP totals.[3]

Appropriations laws and conference reports typically do not specify appropriations levels for most Everglades restoration activities. Rather, the

Administration's budget request identifies restoration funding totals for the Administration's request and for the previous fiscal year.[4] Actual expenditure information for previous appropriations is tracked by the South Florida Ecosystem Restoration Task Force. A summary of funding for both CERP and non-CERP activities within DOI and the Corps is provided below in *Table 1*.

DOI Funding

Funding within the Interior and Environment bill is allotted to four agencies within DOI: the National Park Service (NPS), the Fish and Wildlife Service (FWS), the U.S. Geological Survey (USGS), and the Bureau of Indian Affairs (BIA). Within these agencies, two types of Everglades funding are often highlighted: funding for CERP and funding for the Modified Waters Delivery Project for Everglades National Park (also known as "Mod Waters"). [5] Funding for CERP is typically provided to NPS and FWS, while funding for the Modified Waters deliveries project is provided to NPS. Although Mod Waters is technically a non-CERP project, it is widely considered to be a keystone project for Everglades restoration, including CERP. DOI funding totals for FY2006-FY2014 are shown in *Table 1*.

**Table 1. Corps and DOI Funding for Everglades Restoration
(thousands of dollars)**

	FY2007	FY2008	FY2009	ARRA	FY2010	FY2011	FY2012	FY2013 Estimate	FY2014 Proposed
DOI	75,152	87,355	128,862	23,264	79,424	70,600	99,884	69,803	95,000
CERP	8,481	8,383	9,459	-	8,449	8,401	8,347	8,376	8,000
Non-CERP	66,671	78,972	119,403	23,264	70,975	62,199	91,537	61,427	87,000
Corps	157,553	112,694	115,712	95,412	167,364	131,066	142,486	88,880	88,000
CERP	64,000	64,000	83,640	87,896	119,966	79,860	57,886	n/a	57,000
Non-CERP	93,553	48,694	32,072	7,516	47,398	41,108	84,600	n/a	31,000
Total	232,705	200,049	244,574	118,676	246,788	201,666	242,370	158,683	183,000

Source: CRS estimates based on Congressional Budget Justifications for the U.S. Department of the Interior and Army Corps of Engineers, FY2006-FY2014.

Notes: DOI funding includes funding for the National Park Service, the Fish and Wildlife Service, the U.S. Geological Survey, and the Bureau of Indian Affairs. "ARRA" represents funding under the American Recovery and Reinvestment Act (P.L. 110-5). For FY2013, no funding breakdown for CERP and Non-CERP funding for the Corps was available.

The FY2014 Administration request for Everglades funding included $95 million in DOI funding for Everglades restoration, including $8 million for CERP projects and $87 million for non-CERP projects. No funding was requested for Mod Waters, which is expected to be completed in FY2013.[6]

U.S. Army Corps of Engineers Funding

Funding for Corps Everglades restoration projects in the Energy and Water Development bill is listed under project-level headings in the Corps Construction account. Currently, these projects include the Central and Southern Florida Project, Kissimmee River Restoration, and Everglades and South Florida Restoration. Historically, funding was also included for two other areas, Florida Keys Water Quality Improvement and the Modified Waters Deliveries Project.[7] Corps funding is directed toward planning and construction of projects authorized under CERP and other authorities. Within Corps totals, funding for CERP is considered a key benchmark for Everglades restoration commitment and progress.

Table 1 shows funding totals for the Corps in recent fiscal years and the FY2014 President's request. For FY2014, the President's budget request for Corps Everglades restoration work for FY2014 was $88 million. While this funding level was below previous years, the Administration has noted that unobligated funds from prior years are also expected to be spent in FY2014.

Funding Trends

Federal funding totals for restoration activities in the Everglades ecosystem have been collected since the early 1990s. Overall, since FY1993, the federal investment in Everglades restoration is estimated to have exceeded $4.5 billion. From FY1993 through FY2000, federal appropriations for Everglades restoration activities totaled more than $1.2 billion. More recently, from the enactment of CERP in FY2000 through FY2013, total federal funding exceeded $3.2 billion, with more than $900 million of that total going to federal CERP projects. Overall, average federal funding since the enactment of CERP has increased, from approximately $159 million per year before enactment of CERP, to $251 million per year since CERP was enacted.[8]

Figure 1 shows all Everglades funding since 2001, breaking this funding down between CERP and non-CERP totals. As shown in that figure, while overall funding for Everglades restoration has remained somewhat constant since the enactment of CERP, the distribution between CERP and non-CERP appropriations has changed over time. CERP projects gradually increased from FY2001 to FY2010 (including ARRA). Over the same period, funding for non-CERP projects (such as Mod Waters) decreased from their earlier levels. Finally, over the last two years, overall spending has decreased as project construction has progressed and new authorizations have yet to be provided.

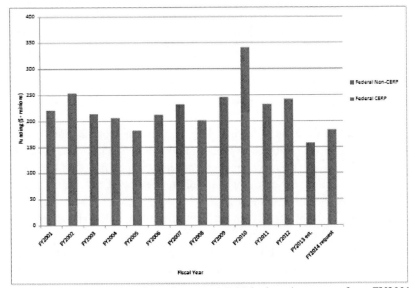

Source: CRS estimates based on Corps and DOI budget documents from FY2001-FY2014.

Notes: FY2010 includes additional funding under P.L. 111-5 (ARRA). Some totals for non-CERP funding may not match with previous totals due to inconsistencies in reported funding levels between the President's budget and the crosscut budget documents.

Figure 1. Estimated Federal Everglades Restoration Funding.

Comparing Federal and State Funding

Comparisons between federal and state funding levels are complicated for a number of reasons. As previously noted, CERP funding is to be cost shared equally between the federal government and nonfederal entities in the state of

Florida. Many view the status and amount of federal CERP funding relative to nonfederal funding for this initiative as an important indicator of the federal government's commitment to Everglades restoration. While the state has invested considerable funding in CERP, much of this funding is for land acquisition related to the expected "footprints" of future CERP projects, rather than funding for existing federal projects which have been authorized by Congress.

Nonfederal CERP expenditures are ostensibly tracked in several reports, including a crosscut budget report prepared annually by the South Florida Ecosystem Restoration Task Force. However, this funding is not formally "credited" by the Corps toward CERP project cost shares until a number of requirements have been met. These requirements include completion of a Project Implementation Report (PIR) and authorization for construction of the project by Congress, as well as signing of a project partnership agreement, or PPA.

Thus, although some reference large nonfederal contributions toward CERP, the proportion of these expenditures that have been formally credited toward CERP is actually much smaller. Indeed, it is possible that, depending on subsequent actions of the Corps and Congress, some of the aforementioned funds will never be credited under CERP.

The magnitude of the difference between initial state expenditures and amounts actually credited under CERP results in a wide range of reported state funding levels for CERP. For instance, the state of Florida's annual crosscut budget previously estimated that from 2001 to 2011, it spent approximately $3 billion on CERP. However, actual credited expenditures from federal and state entities over the same period have been reported by the Corps to be very similar, and a 2012 National Research Council (NRC) review noted that all state expenditures for authorized CERP projects (i.e., projects authorized in WRDA 2000 and WRDA 2007) exceeded federal expenditures by $270 million as of 2011.[9]

The same report estimated that another $584 million in state expenditures would be available for crediting if the expected next "round" of CERP projects is authorized by Congress. Thus, the total amount expended by the state of Florida that may be credited to all future CERP projects ranges widely, depending on which assumptions are used. Future legislative actions, including project authorizations, may be an important factor in determining the exact amount of state funding that is actually eligible for crediting. (For more information, see "Challenges," below.)

IMPLEMENTATION PROGRESS/CHALLENGES

Congress has mandated several major reports that include detailed evaluations of Everglades restoration. NRC reviews of Everglades restoration are published biennially and a report was most recently published in 2012; CERP reports to Congress are published every five years and was most recently completed in 2010.[10] Both reports outline accomplishments and challenges related to CERP and non-CERP projects.

Since passage of CERP in 2000, progress has been made on Everglades restoration for both CERP and non-CERP projects, including construction of pilot projects and initiation of several other construction projects. As discussed below, some of the non-CERP "foundation" projects are nearing completion. Additionally, in recent years many have noted an increase in momentum for Everglades restoration as several projects moved from the planning to construction phase. Most of these projects have seen increases in federal appropriations.

In addition to progress on construction, baseline information and processes have also been established, the scientific understanding of many of the uncertainties associated with Everglades restoration has improved, and a programmatic structure is in place to facilitate future projects. Selected CERP and nonCERP accomplishments as of 2013 are noted below.

Accomplishments[11]

- Purchase of more than 60% of total land required under CERP.
- Design and installation of four CERP pilot projects authorized in WRDA 2000.
- Initiation of construction on the Picayune Strand restoration project (authorized in WRDA 2007), which is expected to restore 55,000 acres of wetlands. The first phase of this project is expected to be complete in 2013.
- Initiation of construction on the Site 1 Impoundment Project (authorized in WRDA 2007), which is expected to provide for 13,280 acre-feet of water storage and prevent saltwater intrusion. The first phase of this project is expected to be completed in 2013.
- Initiation of construction for the C-44 Reservoir and Stormwater Treatment Area (STA) component of the Indian River Lagoon-South

Project (authorized in WRDA 2007), which is expected to store approximately 50,000 acre-feet of stormwater. This project is expected to be completed in 2018.

- Completion of PIRs by the Corps for four projects: the C-111 Spreader Canal; Biscayne Bay Coastal Wetlands; C-43 West Basin Storage Reservoir, and Broward County water preserve areas.
- Initiation of expedited construction by the state of Florida on four projects: Loxahatchee River Watershed, Lakeside Ranch STA, C-111 Spreader Canal, and Biscayne Bay Coastal Wetlands.

Selected Non-CERP Accomplishments

- Initiation of construction of the 1-mile bridge component of the Mod Waters Project, which is expected to improve water deliveries to Everglades National Park. This project is expected to be completed in 2013.
- Completion of three of four phases of the Kissimmee River Restoration Project, which is expected to reconnect the river with its historical flood plain and better restore more natural flows.

Challenges

Outside reviewers, including the NRC, have noted the relatively slow pace of Everglades restoration compared to the ambitious timetables laid out in original program documents.[12] These observers have acknowledged that while there has been some progress in the Everglades, implementation of actual restoration projects receiving federal and state funds has been considerably slower than expected.

At the same time, estimated costs for Everglades restoration have gone up significantly. While CERP was originally estimated to cost a total of $8.2 billion (2000 dollars) in funding over 30 years, more recent estimates indicate that CERP will cost $13.5 billion (2009 dollars), and have extended the expected timeline for implementation to 50 years.[13] Stated reasons for these cost and schedule changes include inflation, changes to project design, and funding streams that were less than originally expected.

As of 2013, no major CERP project receiving federal funds had been completed, and the majority of projects outlined in earlier plans had yet to be initiated. Many of the projects envisioned in earlier program documents are either unauthorized, or else require amendments to their original authorization to proceed further.[14] As of 2013, 10 of the 45 project implementation reports expected under CERP had been finalized or completed in draft form. Of these 10 projects, only four have been authorized by Congress and have had construction initiated. In several cases, CERP projects have yet to be authorized by Congress, but nonfederal construction work had begun.

Another challenge going forward for Everglades restoration may be the status of potential new project authorizations under the Water Resources Development Act (WRDA). Originally, CERP envisioned regular enactment of WRDAs and associated inclusion of CERP projects as they were studied and recommended to Congress. However, since 2000, one WRDA has been enacted (2007). S. 601, the Water Resources Development Act of 2013, would authorize the four Everglades restoration projects with completed PIRs for construction: the C-111 Spreader Canal; Biscayne Bay Coastal Wetlands; C-43 West Basin Storage Reservoir, and Broward County water preserve areas.

Absent new authorizations, there is no clear way for federal work on Everglades restoration under CERP to proceed, and construction may slow considerably from its current pace as existing projects wind down and the Corps is not authorized to expend funds and match prior state expenditures for some projects. Such a scenario would likely delay CERP further relative to the current expected timeline.

Other challenges to Everglades restoration have been noted by outside reviewers and others. These challenges include ongoing issues associated with water quality in the Everglades and south Florida, the adequacy of some restoration efforts in recreating historical hydrologic conditions, and ongoing degradation of species and ecosystems in south Florida, which has in some cases accelerated in recent years.

End Notes

[1] This figure represents the estimated cost to the federal government in October 2009 dollars according to the Corps. See U.S. Army Corps of Engineers, Comprehensive Everglades Restoration Plan, 2010 Report to Congress. Available at http://www.sfrestore.org/documents/index.html. Hereinafter 2010 CERP Report to Congress.

[2] In addition to the Corps and DOI, the South Florida Ecosystem Restoration Task Force also tracks funds that are provided to the National Oceanic and Atmospheric Administration, the U.S. Environmental Protection Agency, and the U.S. Department of Agriculture. However,

in its annual budget request, the Administration typically only tracks "nonCERP" funding for the Corps and DOI.

[3] As previously noted, some funds not discussed in this report are tracked under the "non-CERP" heading because of their contribution to Everglades restoration. This includes funds for the Environmental Protection Agency (also in the Interior and Environment appropriations bill), the National Oceanic and Atmospheric Administration (Commerce, Justice, and State, the Judiciary, and Related Agencies appropriations bill), and the U.S. Department of Agriculture (U.S. Department of Agriculture and Related Agencies appropriations). For additional information, see crosscut budget documents available at http://www.sfrestore.org/documents/index.html.

[4] Thus, these totals often lag behind final enacted appropriations.

[5] The Modified Waters Deliveries Project is an ecosystem restoration project in south Florida designed to improve water delivery to Everglades National Park.

[6] Prior to FY2009, this funding was provided both to the Corps and to DOI.

[7] As noted above, in recent years Mod Waters funding has been provided solely to DOI. Florida Keys Water Quality Improvement was completed in FY2009.

[8] CRS analysis of departmental data for FY1993-FY2013. These totals are for Corps and DOI restoration work only.

[9] Committee on Independent Scientific Review of Everglades Restoration, National Research Council, Progress Toward Restoring the Everglades: The Fourth Biennial, Washington, DC, 2012, http://www.nap.edu/catalog.php? record_id=13422. Hereafter Fourth Biennial Review.

[10] See footnotes 1 and 9.

[11] Accomplishments are as of 2013.

[12] See for example, Committee on Independent Scientific Review of Everglades Restoration, National Research Council, Progress Toward Restoring the Everglades: The Third Biennial Review, Washington, DC, 2010, pp. 64-68, https://download.nap.edu/catalog. php?record_id=12988. Hereinafter referred to as the Third Biennial Review.

[13] According to the Corps, the increased cost estimates since 2000 are attributed to (1) $3.63 billion in inflation adjustments; and (2) $1.63 billion in price /scope changes.

[14] While WRDA 2000 conditionally authorized 10 projects, these projects will reportedly need to have their authorizations amended due to substantive changes in project scope.

INDEX